THE BIRDS OF MINORCA

ENRIC RAMOS

THE BIRDS
OF MINORCA

Drawings by Rafael VIDAL
Translation by Elizabeth HUTCHINSON
and Neus PRETO

EDITORIAL MOLL
MALLORCA

First printing: June 1996
Second printing: May 2000
Photos: © Rafael Vidal and Fèlix de Pablo
Drawings: © Rafael Vidal

© of the text by Enric Ramos

© EDITORIAL MOLL
Torre de l'Amor, 4
07001 Palma de Mallorca

Depòsit Legal: PM-979-2000
I.S.B.N.: 84-273-0761-6

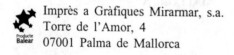

Imprès a Gràfiques Mirarmar, s.a.
Torre de l'Amor, 4
07001 Palma de Mallorca

This book is dedicated to my grandparents Magdalena and Miquel, to my aunt Aguedet, to Margalida Barceló and to Bel Oliver, without doubt they have tolerated and loved me more than anyone in the world.

So far.

Enric.

To my parents

Rafael

PROLOGUE

Amongst the oldest memories that I have of Minorca, during springtime of the late seventies, I have the image of my first Red-kites, flying through the beautiful island skies, the different green shades of the countryside and hills, steep river banks and flat areas. For a tourist like myself who wanted to escape from everyday life, this presented itself as the perfect menu.

A few years later when I resided on the island, it was due to one of the authors of this book that I enjoyed for the first time (aided by a telescope), the visions of a paused and peaceful group of birds swimming in S'Albufera d'Es Grau.

The relationship between professor and pupil has turned into a friendship and professional collaboration during the years that have gone by.

I feel that I am not the best person to make a criticism of this book. For this purpose there are specialized people.

My gratitude to the authors who have offered me this possibility will consist solely in a few comments in order to put the reader in the picture.

A book of this consistency on ornithology of Minorca can only be accomplished by: constant and methodical work, many years of compiling data from different sources, one's own observation, and scientific ringing, contacts and continuous verifications, serious investigations intermingled with an artistic vision, product of passion and curiosity that worldwide naturalists share and express throughout the world. Minorca, thanks to its natural environment and privileged culture, is home to many people who hold these interests. Let's hope that the changes taken place on the island during the past years will not impoverish this patrimony.

On the other hand, a book like this fits into the present needs of an island which is fighting for its future. Any efforts to make the biological and ecological diversity known would help to understand its nature. Without doubt it contributes to maintain its natural wealth. This book also enables one to learn to observe, to get to know and to love birds, to rediscover the pleasure of walking, to acquire the habit of patience and respectful attitudes...

This book, like many others, together with the dedication of people and groups should help to contribute to the Minorcans (especially regarding the Administration) environmental education and motivation, in order to develop coherent attitudes contributing with true contents to the project of The Biosphere Reserve, leaving commercial interests aside.

Begoña Okiñena
Professor of Biology
Institut d'EE.MM.
J. Ramis i Ramis de Maó

PREFACE

Dear readers,

The book you are holding is the product of 14 years of passion and love for these beautiful living creatures known as birds. This book is the result of many days out in the countryside observing and ringing, of reading, travelling and exchanging information. So therefore it is a duty and a great pleasure for me to write this book.

It is not in anyway a guide (for bird identification) as there are many good ones available on the market, instead the object of this book is purely informative, but rigorous, regarding the present knowledge of species that live or spend part of their lives in Minorca.

The meaning is for it to cover two aspects: 1, the updating of previous publications on Minorcan birdlife, 2, to offer to the public, (initiated or not in ornithology), a comprehensive and descriptive piece of work. If we can motivate people to get to know "in situ" one of the most important natural values present on the island, to actively participate and preserve them, our efforts will be amply fulfilled.

Enric Ramos

Palma, December 1993.

GENERAL NOTIONS ABOUT BIRDS

What is a bird?

Birds are vertebrates of constant and high body temperature (generally between 42 and 45°C), oviparous (they reproduce by laying eggs), the body is covered with feathers and the front limbs are transformed into wings, this fact enables them to fly (only a few species such as penguins can't fly due to atrophy or modifications of their wings).

Flight is achieved by a series of complex anatomical and physiological adjustments not covered in this book, since this is not the aim.

Annual cycle of birds

All birds go through a succession of seasonal changes throughout the year, these changes are basically related to: reproduction, moult and migration (if proceeds). Migratory birds have two clear stages in their cycle: one consists in a state of excitement coinciding with migration periods, and the other laying down fat in certain parts of the body before and in the course of migration. This fat provides the extra energy required during the often long and single flight.

It is now accepted that the only exterior factor that affects the annual cycle is the gradual duration of daylight which changes all through the year.

Reproduction

Birds breed at specific times of year, this varies according to different species and areas, but always coinciding when food is plentiful.

In our latitude the majority of species favour the months of April to June, however during March, July and August some species or individual members can still be found in breeding season. Rare and few are the birds breeding outside these periods, none the less this matter will be mentioned in another chapter.

The first step prior to reproduction is: establishing a territory, followed by obtaining a mate, nest-building, copulation, egg-laying, incubation and parental care. In some species parental care continues for some time after the young have left the nest.

Later on in the text we will refer to incubation periods and clutch size of birds breeding in Minorca. Two generalizations can be made, the larger the bird the longer the incubation and the lay is less numerous.

On the other hand, the period between eggshell removal and the chicks' first flight varies according to species. Mostly among passerines the period is under three weeks, yet with the shag (*Phalacrocorax aristotelis*) and some birds of prey this can take over two months. It is understandable, then, that species of "quick reproduction" breed two and in some instances three times each season, taking into account that these birds are more fragile and often become prey, which involves a high rate of infant death. (A large number of passeriformes don't reach their first year of life). Restoration lays are common due to bad weather conditions, nest pillage or disturbances.

Farther ahead (and without going into it in depth) we will speak about the different kinds of reproduction of each species.

Taking into account the behavior of the chick, birds can be divided into two large groups: nidifugous, when the chick leaves the nest soon after birth (most anatids, limicoles and galliformes) and nidicolous, when the chicks stay in their nest until they are completely independent and can manage by themselves. (All other birds come under this category).

We also come across different behaviors and interesting peculiarities when birds are looking for a mate, in general terms we can say that large birds (i.e. birds of prey) tend to stay with the same partner during their lifespan (unless they widow), others such as passeriforms change partners often and some are even polygamous each season.

An interesting peculiarity often found in some birds of prey, is that immature or single males can be found cooperating in building the nest and help to raise the chicks of established pairs.

And finally we would like to point out that during breeding season any disturbances to the nest must be avoided since this is a very critical period and often ends up in total brood failure.

MIGRATION

No doubt, migration is one of the most fascinating chapters in the life of a bird. Books could actually be written just on this subject. Here we will limit ourselves to exposing four basic concepts and some peculiar data on such an interesting phenomenon. For readers wanting to research further into this field, we would recommend the book by Francisco Bernis "Migración en Aves". F. Bernis is considered the father of modern ornithology within the Spanish territory.

Halfway into the 18th century it was thought that birds, as other vertebrates, went into hibernation during the less favourable seasons. Others believed that some species suffered from a metamorphosis and became other birds. It was even thought that some small birds were the fruit of a vegetable or plant.

Today, thanks to ringing techniques and other innovations we have a vast knowledge about migration and specific details of their travels.

Migration may be defined as "a regular large-scale shift of the animal population (birds are not the only animals that migrate) from breeding areas to wintering areas, following an annual cycle and spending the favourable season in the breeding zone.

Not all bird species are migratory but in Europe and the Mediterranean area most of the species migrate. For instance, in Minorca more than 80% are total or partial migrants. Birds that never leave their territory (with trips of under 100 km) are called sedentary or residents.

We must make a differentiation between migration and other non-migratory habits that involve movement for certain species or particular individuals.

The word migration only applies when it is a biological phenomenon of instinctive nature, which consists in a large-scale shift of the population with exact periodicity in time and space and impulses an alternative antagonism regarding the weather conditions in both alternative areas of residence. Obviously this involves two trips, the spring trip that takes birds to the breeding area, and the trip to the wintering area (or winter quarters).

The longest and most spectacular migrations are performed by birds that breed in the polar regions of both hemispheres, those areas that suffer from harsher weather conditions. On the contrary, established birds around equatorial and jungle regions have little or no tendency to migrate, since the weather and food conditions are stable all through the year (except the rainy season).

Therefore the percentage of migratory species and migrant individuals of the same species depends on the latitude where they are established. Closer to the poles more migratory species and specimens can be found, particularly in the northern hemisphere, since in the south other biogeographic factors have to be considered. A clear example is the Robin (*Erithacus rubecula*). In Scandinavia most breeding Robins are migratory, whereas in Central Europe only about 50% migrate, and in the Mediterranean latitudes all breeding Robins are resident.

Centering our attention on Europe and Africa, migratory routes follow the pattern indicated below (see map 1, page 17)

The autumn migrating birds tend to travel from north to south, and during spring migration the other way round, they travel from south to north. In effect, and to be exact, due to land disposition, the routes taken are SW-NE (in the autumn migration) and NE-SW in the spring migration. During autumn/winter Minorca receives (due to its geographical position) birds travelling south and the ones who spend winter here.

During spring-summer birds flying north stopover on the island while the ones that come to spend summer tend to arrive back in spring.

Many birds migrate south, well before food and weather conditions force them to do so (i.e. some warblers and other passeriformes), while others do not move until they are forced by snow or icy conditions (ducks and many aquatic birds).

Migration routes are spread out over a wide front, but there are favourite landmarks always used by many species such as certain coastlines or "mountain necks".

Gliding species (which take advantage of thermic currents for movement), avoid long distances over the sea, since at sea there are not favourable conditions for gliding. Many birds of prey tend to concentrate in large groups on strategic points where the overseas crossing is reduced to a minimum (Gibraltar is a clear example of this factor).

It is quite common for some species in our area to take the spring migration through western routes, and the autumn migration via eastern areas. In other species it is the opposite way around (the imaginary marking of these routes resembles an elliptical figure).

MENORCA

Map 1. Arrows pointing south represent winter migration, and pointing north spring migration.

The great majority of spring migrants travel through Minorca during the months of April and May. And the autumn migrants between September and November. However, there are always individuals or groups of early or late migrants that make it possible to watch such birds almost at any time of year.

The average distance travelled by migratory species varies in each case. In our area (Europe-Africa) we can differentiate two types: species of short distances known as pre-saharan, coming from the north and central parts of Europe where they breed in summer and spend winters in the Mediterranean countries; and the other type

(Grus grus)

are the long distance migrators, known as South-Saharan that breed in Europe and spend winters in central or South Africa, travelling in some instances over 10.000 km per trip.

The average travelling speed varies according to the species, but generally we can say that spring migration is faster than autumn migration, since birds need to arrive early to the breeding areas in order to secure a good territory.

Some species might do the trip in a single flight even if they fly over land, others will spread out flying periods with occasional stops to eat and rest.

Many birds can cross the Mediterranean in one day, at an average speed of 50 km/h, this fact has been proved with scientific ringing, but each species has its own strategy to face the hard test of migration.

There are day migrants and night migrants, among day migrants we have the birds of prey, doves, herons, storks etc..

And robins, warblers, blackbirds and shrikes prefer traveling by night. Other species will travel by day or night indiscriminately.

During the day birds keep their bearings by the sun, and at night they are guided by the stars. Recently it has been demonstrated that terrestrial magnetism plays an important role in guidance. The knowledge and identification of the local geography are important as well and explain how on many occasions the same bird will go back to the same area and will even use the same nest year after year.

Some species travel alone such as birds of prey, hoopoe, cuckoo etc.; others do it in flocks, like ducks, lapwings and many other waders, also starlings. And others travel in family groups.

Migration is always a very hard experience; many youngsters perish from exhaustion or depredation in the course of their first trip.

As mentioned before, migration is not determined by the weather but by the length of daylight. This factor (photoperiod) puts into operation a couple of glands which in a way of answer segregate a hormone which among other things produces in the bird a state of excitement which initiates the start of migration.

During stopovers migrant birds have to lay down fat reserves. Fat is a particularly good source of energy. Just before starting their trip many birds double their normal weight.

Moult

Consists of an other important phenomenon in the annual cycle of a bird's life. Feathers wear out and have to be replaced periodically. This total or partial replacement of feathers is what is called Moult.

During moult there is an important change in the animal's metabolism which provokes an increase in the stress level affecting the animal's vulnerability.

On larger birds the loss of feathers is gradual and prolonged, in some species it can take over one year. The others moult at least yearly or every two years.

The anseriforms (swans, geese and ducks) go through a flightless period during moulting, for this reason during moulting they concentrate in safe areas where food is easy to obtain. In general the moulting process consists of a total post-nuptial moult, and an incomplete spring moult, this varies according to the individual's age. For instance most young birds moult completely in autumn or winter.

Birds moult in favourable conditions integrated with their other biological cycles, such as migration and breeding, avoiding a simultaneous occurrence. Each species and population has its own moult strategy, adapted to their environmental and biological needs.

The resident species do not have the need to moult quickly since they don't have to migrate. Summer migrators must moult very quickly, prior to their departure, in order to have new and effective feathers ready for migration. It is so, that in most cases, moult starts soon after nest-building, and is completed just before migration. Others don't moult until they reach their winter quarters, etc..

SCIENTIFIC RINGING

The purpose of ringing wild birds is to obtain a biological and ecological study of the various species. Through this technique, the following information can be obtained:

1.- Migratory routes, breeding areas, winter and rest quarters.

2.- To study migration and relevant information of their travels.

3.- Studies of young and post-nuptial break up or dispersion.

4.- To find out the average longevity, the survival chart and the process of renovation of different species. This information can help assess the ecological impact on any group of individuals.

5.- To get to know the main mortality reasons for each species. With this information, protection can be demanded for endangered species.

6.- To study the morphology, biometry, and moult of the bird population and their relation with migration.

On the other hand, through ringing, scarce, accidental or hidden species can be found.

Birds can be caught by innocuous methods and ringing can also be performed on chicks directly in their nests. Certainly the most effective methods of capture are the "japanese nets".

It is important to know that the practice of ringing and use of the above methods are absolutely forbidden without special authorization. This authorization can only be obtained by reference from a well established group, and when the candidate has proved to be skilled and knowledgeable.

In 1983 the first ringing group of wild birds of Minorca was founded, forming part of the ornithological department of G.O.B.

Since then over 30.000 birds have been ringed, belonging to 120 different species. In Minorca it is the only group authorized by both the central and local administration.

All ringing groups within the Spanish territory are directly dependent of «Oficina de anillamiento de aves» of ICONA.

Icona provides the rings and collects and centralizes all data received periodically from the different ringing groups all over Spain. This office publishes an annual booklet.

All tags/rings within the Spanish territory have the following inscription: MINIS-TERIO DE AGRICULTURA, Icona - Madrid, and a number (sometimes followed by a word/letter), each nº is different and identifies each individual bird.

2. Ringing

The percentage of birds recovered outside the ringing areas varies according to the species and varies between 1 and 10% for the larger birds (sea gulls, shags, and birds of prey etc.) while on smaller birds the percentage drops to around 2 ‰. From this information we can gather the large effort needed in order to get a result.

Through this book, we would like to appeal to the public, that upon finding a ringed bird, to contact G.O.B. C/. Isabel II, 42. Maó. Tel. 350762 or the Conselleria d'Agricultura i Pesca local offices.

When possible it is important to provide the following information:

- Its species, the condition in which it was found (alive, dead, run over by a car, hunted, only the ring has been found etc..), the date and place where found.

Once the information has been processed, the original details of the bird and a thank you letter is sent to the person concerned.

BIRD WATCHING

To start off in the world of ornithology there is no need to have specific studies. All one needs is the time and the will to do so. The basic question is to be able to identify species seen during outings.

This book, as previously stated, doesn't pretend to be a guide, therefore anybody wishing to bird-watch needs to acquire a guide, which can be easily found in any bookshop. All guides have the necessary indications in order to identify each species successfully. It is a good idea to go with an experienced bird watcher during the first outings.

A good ally would be a pair of binoculars, and if possible a telescope. When buying it is always advisable to get other bird watchers' opinions in order to make the best choice amongst all the products on the market.

Areas of Particular Interest for Bird Watching

Birds can practically be found all round the island, but there are obviously certain spots where due to their particular characteristics, one can find a larger amount of specimens and species. The wetlands, for instance, are areas with a larger diversity of species. S'Albufera des Grau and Son Bou-Atalis are areas where a larger number of species can be found, but obviously not all.

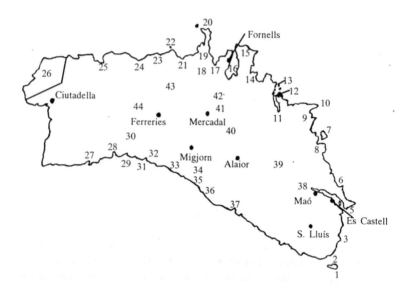

MAP 2: Most favourable areas for bird/watching.

1: Illa de l'Aire. 2: Area of Punta Prima (to Alcaufar). 3: Areas of Rafalet and Cala de S. Esteve . 4: Port of Maó. 5: Mola of Maó. 6: Coastal area between Cap Negre and Cala Mesquida, wet area of Mesquida and the near moors. 7: Illa d'en Colom. 8: Area of S'Albufera des Grau (pine woods, dunes, beach, meadows, gorget) 9: Bassa de Morella. 10: Favàritx area. 11: Salines d'Addaia 12: port d'Addaia and area of Mongofre. 13: Islets of Addaia. 14: Area of Son Saura Nord ("Son Parc") 15: Mola of Fornells 16: Area of Fornells 17: Area of Tirant (wet area and dunes). 18: Basses de Lluriac. 19. Area of Cavalleria, Farraguts and Sta. Teresa. 20: Cap de Cavalleria and islet of Porros 21: Binimel.là (wet area) and Cala Pregonda. 22: Islets Bledes. 23: Ets Alocs and Es Milocar. 24: Area of Muntanya Mala, Falconera and Xevagues. 25: Area of La Vall (coast, beach, wet areas, woods, moors and plains). 26: Area of Cala Morell - Pta. Nati and Cap de Minorca. 27: Son Saura South (wet area and moors). 28: Area of Macarelleta (coast and small steep river banks). 29: Area of Cala Galdana: coast line and wet area. 30. Steep river bank d'Algendar. 31: Trebelúger: wetlands and coast. 32: Steep river banks of Trebalúger and Son Fideu. 33: Binigaus steep river bank. 34: Steep river banks of: Sa Vall - Son Boter and d'es Bec. 35: Son Bou: beach, dunes and meadows. 36: Llucalari 37: Cala en Porter: coast, wet area and steep river bank. 38: Orchards and St. Joan's river bank 39: Area of Es Puntarró, steep riverbank and woods 40: Wooded area Sa Roca. 41: Area of el Toro 42: Wooded areas of Binigurdó and surroundings. 43: Sta. Àgueda and surroundings. 44: Area of Es Pla Verd.

The most favourable areas are pointed out on Map 2. Later on in the book the best areas are described along with each species.

The most favourable times of year for watching a larger number of species are undoubtedly spring and autumn, due to the birds' migratory movements.

Songs and Calls

The songs and calls of birds are very useful for their identification. Often this is the only way to identify species which are similar in appearance and of discrete habits.

Most species produce their songs and calls during the spring and summer (most males' songs are used to attract a female). The songs of different species are often clearly different. Some birds sing when well hidden, like the nightingale; others, like some warblers, sing while they move from place to place. The Thekla Lark and the Fan-tailed warbler have a very distinctive song.

Birds produce other sounds to convey messages to other individuals, such as alarm calls. These particular calls can often and with practice be used to identify the species.

One can find tapes and records with the songs of all European species, which are worthwhile acquiring. Under the chapter on recommended books there are references to these products.

CHECK-LIST OF ALL BIRDS REGISTERED IN MINORCA AND THEIR STATUS ON THE ISLAND.
(Updated December 93)

In the next pages, there is a list of all birds registered on the island, indicating their present status. The systematic order established by K.H. Voous in 1978 can be used by following these key codes:

S: Sedentary or local resident species all year round (there may be partial substitutions of population according to season, and in many cases whole or part dispersion of the young population outside the island, and even of occasional adults after breeding season).

E: Summer visitor, present in breeding season (spring-summer).

M: Passage migrant (spring-autumn).

H: Winter visitor only found between autumn and spring.

A: Rare, vagrant exceptional visitor (at any time of year).

F/?: Species without enough information to judge their status on the island.

N   : Common breeder.

(Np): Possible breeder not enough information to assure it.

(NP): Probable breeder. Not proved.

NA : Rare/accidental breeder.

I   : Species introduced.

Ex : Extinct as breeders.

The following symbols regarding population within the different species and their relative or absolute abundance are added.

e: Scarce, between 1 to 100

m: Moderate, between 101 to 1.000

a: Abundant, over 1.001

Examples:

67. *Pandion haliaetus* (Osprey): Se, Me, He; Ne

Se: Means that the Osprey is present on the Island all year round (it's not been verified as being the same individuals), in small numbers (probably no more than an average of 10 or 15 specimens)

Me:Other individuals visit at migration times.

He:Some European specimens spend winters on the island (this has been discovered due to the recuperation of ringed birds, and the increase of winter population).

Ne: Some pairs breed on the island (it is suspected that 1 year-old youngsters leave the island in autumn and may or may not return at a later stage).

209. *Acrocephalus melanopogon* (Moustached warbler): Se or m; Me?, He?, Ne o m.

This bird is present all year round, and a few breed on the Island. It is not clear if they are winter visitors, if so there are only a small amount. It is to be verified whether all or part of the young leave the island after breeding. These details are explained under the corresponding text.

248. *Sturnus vulgaris* (Starling): Ma, Ha, EA

Here we can see that the starling is an abundant passage migrant and winter visitor (well over 50.000 specimens). They are scarcely observed in summer (only 3 or 4), and are considered accidental during this time of year.

GAVIIDAE
1. Red-throated Diver: A
2. Great Northern Diver: A?

PODICIPEDIDAE
3. Little Grebe: Se or m, Mm, Im; Ne
4. Great Crested Grebe: Me,Ie
5. Slavonian Grebe: F, A
6. Black-necked Grebe: Mm, He

DIOMEDEIDAE
7. Cory's Shearwater: Ea, Mm or a, Hm, Na

8. Balearic Shearwater: Em or a, Ma, Nm or a (ssp yelkouan)

HYDROBATIDAE
9. Storm Petrel: S (e or m), N (e or m), M?
10. Leach's Petrel: A

SULIDAE
11. Gannet: Me, He

PHALACROCORACIDAE
12. Cormorant: Mm, Hm
13. Balearic Shag: Sm or a, Nm

ARDEIDAE
14. Bittern: Me
15. Little Bittern: Me, Ee? NA?
16. Night Heron: Mm, Ee
17. Squacco Heron: Me, EA
18. Cattle Egret: Mm, He, Ee
19. Little Egret: Mm, He, Ee
20. Great white Egret: A, He?
21. Grey Heron: Mm, Hm, Ee or m
22. Purple Heron: Me or m, Ee, Ex?

CICONIIDAE
23. Black Stork: A or Me
24. White Stork: Me

THRESKIORNITHIDAE
25. Glossy Ibis: A or Me
26. Spoonbill: A

PHOENICOPTERIDAE
27. Greater Flamingo: A or Me, He or A

ANATIDAE
28. Mute Swan: A

29. Whooper Swan: A
30. Bewick's Swan: A
31. Bean Goose: A
32. Greylag Goose: He
33. Barnacle Goose: A
  -. Ruddy Shelduck: A?
34. Shelduck: He, Me, EA
  -. Mandarin Duck: A
35. Wigeon: Mm, Hm
36. Gadwall: Me, He
37. Teal: Mm, Hm
38. Mallard: Sm, Mm or a, Hm or a, Nm
39. Pintail: Me, He
40. Garganey: Mm
41. Blue-winged Teal: A
42. Shoveler: Mm, He or m
43. Red-crested Pochard: A
44. Pochard: Mm, Hm, Ee or A
45. Ferruginous Duck: A, Me? H?
46. Tufted Duck: Me, He
47. Scaup: A
48. Gider: A
49. Common Scoter: A
50. Velvet Scoter: A
51. Goldeneye: A
52. Red-Breasted Merganser: A, He?
  -. Goosander: A?
  -. Smew: A?

ACCIPITRIDAE
53. Honey Buzzard: Mm
54. Black Kite: Me, He or A, EA
55. Red Kite: Se or m, Me or m, He, Ne
56. Egyptian Vulture: Se or m, Me, He? Ne
57. Black Vulture: A

58. Short-toed Eagle: Me
59. Marsh Harrier: Mm, He, EA; Ex?
60. Hen Harrier: Me or m, He
61. Montagus Harrier: Me or m
62. Pallid Harrier: A
63. Sparrow Hawk: Me or m, He or m, EA, Ex?
64. Buzzard: Mm or e, He, EA
   – Golden eagle: A?
65. Booted Eagle: Se or m, Me, He?, Ne
66. Bonelli's Eagle: A

PANDIONIDAE
67. Osprey: Se, Me, He; Ne

FALCONIDAE
68. Lesser Kestrel: Me or A; Ex?
69. Kestrel: Sm, Mm or e, He?, Nm
70. Red-footed Falcon: Mm (spring); A (autumn)
71. Merlin: Me or A, He or A
72. Hobby: Me or m, HA
73. Eleonora's Falcon: Me, Ee
74. Lanner: A, He? Me?
75. Peregrine: Se, Me? He? Ne

PHASIANIDAE
76. Red-legged Partridge: Sa, Na
   – Barbary Partridge: I and Ex
   – Francolin: I and Ex
77. Quail: Se or m; Ea, Mm, He or m; Nm or a

RALLIDAE
78. Water Rail: Sm, Me? He?; Nm
79. Spotted Crake: Se? Me, He; Ne?

80. Little Crake: F, Me?
81. Baillon's Crake: F, Me?
82. Corn Crake: F, Me?
83. Moorhen: Sa, Mm. Hm, Nm or a
   – Purple Gallinule: Ex
84. Coot: Sm, Ma, Ha, Nm

GRUIDAE
85. Crane: Me or m; HA

OTIDAE
86. Little Bustard: A

HAEMATOPODIDAE
87. Oystercatcher: Me

RECURVIROSTRIDAE
88. Black-winged Stilt: Ee, Me or m, HA, Ne
89. Avocet: Me or A

BURHINIDAE
90. Stone Curlew: Sa, Mm or e, Hm or e, Nm or a

GLAREOLIDAE
91. Cream-coloured Courser: A
92. Collared Pratincole: Me

CHARADRIIDAE
93. Little ringed Plover: Ee, Mm, HA, Ne
94. Ringed Plover: Mm, He, EA
95. Kentish Plover: Se or m, Mm, He, Ne
96. Golden Plover: Me? He or m
97. Grey Plover: Me, He, EA
98. Lapwing: Mm, Hm or a

SCOLOPACIDAE
99. Knot: Me or A
100. Sanderling: Me or A, He or A
101. Little Stint: Mm, He or A, EA
102. Temmincki's Stint: Me, HA?
103. Curlew Sandpiper: Mm
104. Purple Sandpiper: Me or A, HA
105. Dunlin: Mm, He or A
    – Broad-billed Sandpiper: A?
106. Ruff: Mm, HA
107. Jack Snipe: Me, or m, He or m
108. Snipe: Mm or a; Hm or a
109. Great Snipe: A
110. Woodcock: Mm, Hm or a
111. Black-tailed Godwit: Mm, HA
112. Bar-tailed Godwit: Me or A
113. Whimbrel: Me
114. Slender-billed Curlew: A
115. Curlew: Me, HA
116. Spotted Redshank: Me, or m He or A
117. Redshank: Mm He EA
118. March Sandpiper: Me
119. Green Shank: Mm, HA
120. Green Sandpiper: Mm, HE or A, EA
121. Wood Sandpiper: Mm
122. Common Sandpiper: Se? Mm, He, Ee
123. Turnstone: Me or A

STERCORARIIDAE
124. Great Skua: Me, He
125. Arctic Skua: A

-. Long-tailed Skua: A?
-. Pomarinus: A?

LARIDAE
126. Mediterranean Gull: F, Me or A, He or A
127. Little Gull: F, Me or A, He or A
128. Black-headed Gull: Mm or a Hm or a Ee (Np)
129. Slender-billed Gull: F Me or A
130. Audouin's Gull: Em He Nm
131. Common Gull: F Me or A HA
132. Lesser Black-backed Gull: F, Me, He
133. Yellow-legged Gull: Sa, Na
134. Great Black-backed Gull: A
-. Kittiwake: F, A?

STERNIDAE
135. Gull-billed Tern: Me or m
-. Caspian Tern: A?
136. Sandwich Tern: Me or m He, EA
137. Common Tern: F Me or A, HA
-. Roseate Tern: A?
138. Little Tern: Me or A
139. Whiskered Tern: Me or m
140. Black Tern: Me or m
141. White-winged Black Tern: Me

ALCIDAE
142. Guillemot: A
143. Razorbill: A, HA
144. Puffin: He or A

COLUMBIDAE
145. Rock Dove: Sa Na
146. Stock Dove: F Mm or A?
    Hm or A?
147. Wood Pigeon: Sa Mm?
    Hm, Na
148. Turtle Dove; Ea, Ma, Na

CUCULIDAE
149. Great Spotted Cuckoo: Me
    or A
150. Cuckoo: Em Mm Nm

TYTONIDAE
151. Barn Owl: Sm, Ne or m

STRIGIDAE
152. Scops Owl: Sm, Mm, He
    or m; Nm
153. Little Owl: F, Se? Me, He,
    Ne or A
154. Long-eared Owl: F Se?
    Me, He or A (Np)
-. Tawny Owl: A?
155. Short-eared owl: F Me He

CAPRIMULGIDAE
156. Nightjar: Ee or m, Mm, Ne
    or m

APODIDAE
157. Swift: Ea, Ma, HA, Na
158. Pallid Swift: Ea, Mm or a,
    Nm or a
159. Alpine Swift: Ee or m,
    Mm, Ne or m

ALCEDINIDAE
160. Kingfisher: Mm, He, Ee or
    A (NAp), Ex?

MEROPIDAE
161. Bee-eater: Em, Mm or a,
    Nm

CORACIIDAE
162. Roller: Me

UPPUPIDAE
163. Hoopoe: Sa, Mm or a, Nm
    or a

PICIDAE
164. Wryneck: Mm He or m Ee
    or A? (NAp)

ALAUDIDAE
    – Calandra Lark: A?
165. Short-toed Lark: Ea, Ma,
    Na
166. Lesser Short-toed Lark: F,
    Me or A
167. Thekla Lark: Sa, Na
-. Crested Lark: F A?

-. Woodlark: A?
168. Skylark: Mm or a, Hm or a

HIRUNDINIDAE
169. Sand Martin: Ma
170. Crag Martin: Me or m He or m
171. Swallow: Em or a, Ma, HA, Nm or a
172. Red-Rumped Swallow: Me
173. House Martin: Ea Ma Na

MOTACILLIDAE
174. Richard's Pipit: A
175. Tawny Pipit: Em or a, Mm, Nm or a
176. Tree Pipit: Mm or a
177. Meadow Pipit: Mm or a Ha
178. Red-throated Pipit: Me
179. Rock-water Pipit: Mm Hm
180. Yellow/Blue-headed Wagtail: Ma
181. Grey Wagtail: Mm, Hm
182. Pied-white Wagtail: Ma, Ha

TROGLODYTIDAE
183. Wren: Hm (Np)

PRUNELLIDAE
184. Dunnock (hedge sparrow): Mm or a, Ha
185. Alpine Accentor: Me or m, He or m

TURDIDAE
186. Robin: Ma, Ha
    – Thrush Nightingale: A?
187. Nightingale: Ea, Ma, Na
188. Blue Throat: Me or m, He or m

189. Black Redstart: Ma, Ha
190. Redstart: Ma
191. Whinchat: Ma, HA
192. Stonechat: Sa, Mm or a, Hm or a, Na
193. Wheatear: Ma
194. Black-ear Wheatear: Me or m
195. Black Wheatear: A
196. Rock Thrush: Me
197. Blue Rock Thrush: Sa, M?, H?, Na
198. White's Thrush: A
199. Ring Ouzel: Me, He
200. Blackbird: Sa, Mm or a, Hm or a, Na
201. Fieldfare: Me, He
201. Song Thrush: Ma, Ha
203. Redwing: Mm, Hm
204. Mistle Thrush: Mm, Hm

SYLVIIDAE
205. Cetti's Warbler: Sa, M?, Nm or a
206. Fan-tailed Warbler: Sa, M?, Na
207. Grasshopper Warbler: Mm
208. Saul's Warbler: Ee?, Me?, Ne?, F
209. Moustached Warbler: Se or m, Me?, He?, Ne or m
210. Aquatic Warbler: Me or A
211. Sedge Warbler: Mm
-. Marsh Warbler: Me or A?
212. Reed Warbler: Ee or m, Mm (spring), Ma (autumn), He?, Ne or m
213. Great Reed Warbler: Ee, Mm, Ne
-. Olivaceous Warbler: Me?

214. Icterine Warbler: Mm
215. Melodious Warbler: Me or m
216. Marmora's Warbler: F, Se?, Ne?, Ex?
217. Dartford Warbler: Sm, M?, H?, Nm
218. Spectacled Warbler: Ee, Me?, Ne

219. Subalpine Warbler: Mm or a (NP)
220. Sardinian Warbler: Sa, Me?, Na
221. Orphean Warbler: Me?, F
222. Barred Warbler: A
223. Lesser Whitethroat: Me?, F
224. Whitethroat: Ma
225. Garden Warbler: Ma, NAp
226. Blackcap Warbler: Sm or a, Ma, Ha, NM or a
227. Yellow-browed Warbler: A
228. Arctic Warbler: Me
229. Wood Warbler: Ma (spring), Me or A (autumn)
230. Chiffchaff: Ma, Ha
231. Willow Warbler: Ma (spring), Mm (autumn)
232. Goldcrest: Mm, Hm
233. Firecrest: Sm or a, Me or m, He or m, Nm or a

MUSCICAPIDAE
234. Spotted Flycatcher: Em or a, Ma, Nm or a
235. Red-breasted Flycatcher: A
236. Collared Flycatcher: Me?, F
237. Pied Flycatcher: Ma

PARIDAE
-. Coal Tit: A?

-. Blue Tit: A?
238. Great Tit: Sm or a, Nm or a

TIMALIDAE
-. Bearded Tit: A?

TICHODROMADIDAE
239. Wall Creeper: A, Me?, He?

REMIZIDAE
240. Penduline Tit: Me or m, He or m

ORIOLIDAE
241. Golden Oriole: Me or m

LANIIDAE
242. Red-backed Shrike: Me or A
243. Great Grey Shrike: A
244. Woodchat Shrike: Ea, Ma, Na
-. Masket Shrike: A?

CORVIDAE
-. Magpie: Al?, A?
-. Alpine Chough: A?
245. Chough: A
-. Jackdaw: A?
246. Rook: A
-. Carrion/Hooded Crow: A?

247. Raven: Sm, M?, H?, Ne or
     m

STURNIDAE
248. Starling: Ma, Ha, EA
249. Spotless Starling: Me?,
     He?, F
250. Rose-coloured Starling: A

PASSERIDAE
251. House Sparrow: Sa Na
252. Tree Sparrow: F Me? He?
253. Rock Sparrow: F NA? M?
     H?
254. Snowfinch: A

FRINGILLIDAE
255. Chaffinch: Sa, Ma, Ha, Nm
     or a
256. Brambling: Me, Hm
257. Serin: Me or m, Hm or a
258. Citril Finch: A

259. Greenfinch: Sa, Mm, Hm,
     Na
260. Goldfinch: Sa, Mm or a,
     Hm or a, Na
261. Siskin: Mm or a, Hm or a
262. Linnet: Sa, Ma, Ha
263. Redpoll: AI?, A?
264. Common Crestbill: A
265. Bullfinch: AI?, A?
266. Trumpeter Finch: A
267. Hawfinch: Me, Hm

EMBERIZIDAE
268. Snow Bunting: A
269. Yellow Hammer: A
270. Cirl Bunting: A
-. Rock Bunting: A?
271. Ortolan Bunting: Me or m
272. Red Bunting: Me or m, Hm
273. Corn Bunting: Sa, Me?,
     He?, Na

SUMMARY

- Total number of species found on the island: 273
- Species found all year round: 50 (31 non-passerines and 19 passerines) + 7 probable or irregular.
- Summer visitors: 22 (12 non-passerines and 10 passerines) + 5 probable or irregular.
- Migrant species: 60 (38 non-passerines and 22 passerines) + 8 probable or irregular.
- Vagrants or accidental species: 83 (52 non-passerines and 31 passerines)
- Regular breeders: 64 (35 non-passerines and 29 passerines)
- Possible breeders but not confirmed: 15
- Extinct as breeders: 3 + 5 possible
- Uncertain species: 23

Note: Species of birds in captivity, (seen around villages, towns and fields) have not been mentioned in the book or this previous list, such as chickens, ducks or cocks. We would like to make special of mention of those birds that have escaped and established themselves in the wild (this has happened in Minorca and Majorca with the *Mysiopisitta monachus*), producing a negative impact on the ecological equilibrium of the natural ecosystems.

On the other hand, acquiring birds (or other animals) considered as pets promotes the traffic of species, causing serious problems to the original population. It is recommended not to participate in this type of harmful trade.

APPENDIX:

THE NAMES OF BIRDS IN MINORCA

The folk names given to animals and plants in the various regions represents a linguistic heritage to be cherished.

Problems arise when, talking about a certain species, their denominations can be ambiguous, such as:

a) One name is used for two or more species
or,
b) When one species has various names.

Within Minorca, some species are given a different name in each village, town or rural region (sometimes even within the same town). Also different species are given the same name (because they look alike to an inexpert's eye).

On the other hand, scarce or rare visitors do not have a popular name, since they are unknown to folk.

I would like presently to recall an anecdote that my great-grandmother's brother told me, a man of great knowledge on birds who used to farm and hunt.

Two friendly hunters, both very proud and big-headed came to blows one day in the course of an argument. One of them insisted that Blackbird and Blue rock thrush were two names to designate the same bird, while the other insisted (correctly) that it was two different birds.

In order to avoid such situations and to keep the Minorcan linguistic heritage alive, the team of ornithologists on the island (from all villages!) got together in the fall of 1993, in order to reach a consensus and to list each bird species found on the island with a sole valid name.

It was agreed from then on that these would be the official names and are therefore used in all publications or notices regarding birds of Minorca.

To this effect Tòfol Mascaró (an ornithologist from Alaior), produced a first listing with the existing material, adding the names used in Majorca (more or less "officialized" by the publishing of the ornithological annual of the Balearic Islands) and in Catalan.

Unfortunately, not enough serious field work has been done interviewing a large enough number of farmers, hunters and bird watchers. Consequently we are afraid that some names used in more reduced habitats will have been left out.

The criteria used to select the Minorcan name were as follows:

– To keep names well rooted to the island.

– When there is more than one name:

    1) Avoid possible ambiguity, that could represent confusion.

    2) To favour communication outside the island, choosing names closer to Majorcan and/or Catalan names.

– When coming upon a nameless species in Minorca, an invented name is avoided and the Majorcan or Catalan one is used instead.

In this book, names appear as follows: First the English denomination, followed by the name in Latin (universally used for each species). Second the proposed Minorcan name. Third any other name used on the island. Fourth the Majorcan name. Fifth the standard Catalan name. Sixth the standard Spanish name.

N.P.: Proposed Minorcan name
A.M.: Other Minorcan names
Mall.: Majorcan name
C.: Standard Catalan name
Cast.: Standard Spanish name.

LIST OF SPECIES AND COMMENTS

This section is the main part of the book and goes through every single bird found in Minorca and their actual situation on the island.

It indicates the bird's status (migrant, resident, winter visitor etc.), its migratory habits (dates of arrival and departure), absolute or relative abundance, biotopes and favorable areas on the island, reproduction, feeding habits, and in some cases other interesting data such as geographical distribution and information collected through ringing about the origin and destination of migrants.

Regarding the information on ringing, due to how similar it is in all the Balearic Islands, it is taken into account as a whole.

With respect to the geographical distribution, only the following mentions will be used:

Arctic:- Fauna from tundra and areas of birch on the northern hemisphere.

Cosmopolitan:- Fauna from such a wide area which makes it difficult to establish the origins.

European:- Fauna from the temperate and Mediterranean part of Europe.

Euro-turquestan:- Fauna from the temperate and Mediterranean areas of Europe and south/west Asia.

Holarctic:- Fauna from cold, temperate and sub-tropical regions of the north hemisphere.

Indo-African:- At present the fauna is geographically discontinuous but towards the tertiary and Pleistocene periods it must have extended itself continuously from Mid-Asia to North and Central Africa.

Mediterranean:- Fauna belonging to the Mediterranean areas.

Palearctic:- Fauna from cold, mild and sub-tropical areas of the northern half of the Old World (Eurasia).

Siberian:- Fauna from the boreal region to the palearctic region, especially taiga.

ORDER GAVIIFORMES

FAMILY GAVIIDAE

Red-throated Diver (*Gavia stellata*). N.P.: Calàbria petita;
A.M.: Cabussó petit; Mall: Cabussó petit; C.: Calàbria petita; Cast.:
Colimbo chico.

Bird common of sub-arctic regions, rare winter visitor only during very severe ones. In Minorca we only have references of one specimen embalmed in the Ateneu Museum of Maó, without specific date or place of capture.

Great Northern Diver (*Gavia immer*). N.P.: Calàbria grossa;
A.M.: Cabussó gros; Mall.: Cabussó gros; C.: Calàbria grossa; Cast.:
Colimbo grande.

There are only two bibliographical references about this bird, one captured in January 1917 (preserved at the Ateneu Museum), and an uncertain mention by an ornithologist of the last century.

ORDER PODICIPEDIFORMES

FAMILY PODICIPEDIDAE

Little Grebe (*Tachybaptus ruficollis*). N.P.: Soterí petit; A.M.:
Soterí, Anedó; Mall.: Setmesó; C: Cabusset; Cast.: Zampullín chico
(3) (Photo 1).

The presence of Little Grebe on the island is associated with S'Albufera des Grau; it is estimated that 20/30 pairs actually breed there. They might be found breeding on regular or sporadic bases around Es Prat de Son Bou, Sa Bassa de Morella, Bassa de Lluriac-Tirant, Son Saura North and may be at the mouths of streams where wetlands form, such as La Vall, Cala En Porter or Algendar.

3. Little Grebe (*Tachybaptus ruficollis*)

During migration and winter they are more abundant due to the arrival of winter residents from Europe. Around 150 specimens have been censed during the cold season mostly around S'Albufera. This figure can dramatically change from one year to the next. The preferred food consists of small fish and aquatic invertebrates; they catch their food by immersing their heads in the water (hence the Minorcan name Soterí which means immersing a body in and out of water quickly).

Breeding begins March/April. They build a well hidden nest and lay between 3 and 5 eggs. Mothers carry their chicks among the back feathers.

Great Crested Grebe (*Podiceps cristatus*). N.P.: Soterí gros; A.M.: Soterí blanc, Cabusell; Mall.: Soterí gros; C: Cabussó emplomallat; Cast.: Somormujo Lavanco (**4**).

Aquatic bird of medium size. Scarce winter resident in Minorca. Between September and March it can be found in S'Albufera. Occasionally they have been seen with their nuptial plumage. The maximum number of specimens cited in this area is 13. Other areas where they can be spotted occasionally (in migration or winter periods) are Port of Maó, Port of Fornells, and Addaia.

Their diet is varied, consisting of fish, insects, small frogs, plants, mollusks, etc...

Slavonian Grebe (*Podiceps auritus*). N.P.: Soterí orellut; A.M.: Soterí de galtes blanques; Mall.: Soterí de coll blanc; C: Cabussó orellut; Cast: Zampullín cuellirrojo (**5**).

4. Great Crested Grebe *(Podiceps cristatus)*

Small aquatic bird, scarce presence on the island, in fact there are only 3 observations registered, two in November and one in February. A single specimen and spotted always at S'Albufera.

It is worth pointing out that their winter plumage is very similar to that of the Black-Necked Grebe which is a regular winter resident, and could

5. Slavonian Grebe
(Podiceps auritus)

go unnoticed. However, this species is of Holarctic distribution and only a few arrive in winter to the mediterranean area.

Black-necked Grebe *(Podiceps nigricollis)*. N.P.: Soterí coll negre; A.M.: Soterí gros; Mall.: Soterí coll negre; C.: Cabussó; Cast.: Zampullín cuellinegro **(6)**.

This species is regularly found during migratory periods and in winter, but in small numbers. Observations date from July to early April. S'Albufera des Grau homes about 40 winter residents, this figure tends to increase. Other favourable areas are the Ports of Maó and Fornells. During migration they can be observed sporadically around most wetlands and coastal areas.

The island of Formentera (L'Estany Pudent) homes between 1000 and 4000 specimens during the winter months, and possibly it is the most important Mediterranean winter home for this species. Their behaviour and eating habits are very similar to those of the little grebe although it tends to be more of a marine bird.

6. Black-Necked Grebe
(Podiceps nigricollis)

ORDER PROCELLARIIFORMES

FAMILY DIOMEDEIDAE

Cory's Shearwater (*Calonectris diomedea*). N.P.: Baldritja grossa; A.M.: Baldritxa, baldritja, virot; Mall.: Virot; C.: Baldritja cendrosa. Cast.: Pardela cenicienta (7) Photo 4.

Sea bird, pelagic, spends most of its life at sea, fish and squid are its main diet. Large as a sea gull, having been observed once or twice it is difficult to mistake it, unless for some other species of shearwater, rare or vagrant on the island.

Commonly seen flying over sea surface at fast speed without hardly a flap of wings. In fact they take advantage of air currents that form between waves and move with hardly any waste of energy. During spring and summer they can be seen in groups on the sea surface near the shore and opposite breeding areas. In Minorca their breeding colonies are located along the northern seacliffs.

7. Cory's Shearwater
(*Calonectris diomedea*)

8. Balearic Shearwater
(*Puffinus yelkouan*)

On the south coast they are more scarce and there is only one small colony known.

They take advantage of the often narrow breakages and galleries on the coastal rocky cliff sides, and they use rocks and burrows with a minimum available space for their nest. The nest gives off a very strong and characteristic smell. They lay one single egg that is incubated for approximately 50 days. The parents stay and feed the chick for about 3 months, when fully feathered they literally abandon it; then forced by hunger, it throws itself to sea and hence its hard life commences. Until very recently, farmers around the area of Ciutadella used to collect their eggs for home consumption. During winter they live at sea mostly in the Mediterranean but can reach the Atlantic (a bird ringed in Majorca was found in Senegal).

It is estimated that the breeding population on Minorca is between 1500 and 5000 pairs, the most important in the Balearic Islands.

Balearic Shearwater (*Puffinus yelkouan*). N.P.: Baldritja petita A.M. Baldritja, baldritxa; Mall.: Baldritja; C.: Baldriga pufí; Cast.: Pardela pichoneta **(8)**.

Of very similar habits to cory's shearwater but less abundant in Minorca. Slightly smaller than cory's shearwater and easy to distinguish on flight, since it alternates gliding with flapping of the wings.

It seems to be established that the Balearic specimens form an endemic subspecies (*Puffinus yelkouan mauretanicus*) different from *Puffinus yelkouan yelkouan* with breeding colonies on the eastern Mediterranean coast. The specimens observed during autumn/winter in Minorca are from this last subspecies. Only in 1991 was it confirmed that this bird reproduced on the island, although it had been suspected since 1970. Nests were found in 4 breeding areas of the *Calonectris diomedea*. In fact some pairs use the same holes as the c.d., and seemingly it doesn't provoke rivalry.

Little is known about their biological and ecological behavior.

The total reproduction population is of about 300 pairs, though it could be quite a few more. Occasionally concentrations of about 900 specimens have been observed near the shore.

In fall and winter they scatter widely over the Mediterranean and the Atlantic Ocean. This information has been gathered by the recovery of birds originally ringed in Majorca and Ibiza. Favàritx and Cavalleria are good spots to observe this shearwater, providing you have a good telescope. Obviously the best observations are made at sea from a boat.

Frequently you can observe mixed flocks.

FAMILY HYDROBATIDAE

Storm Petrel (*Hydrobates pelagicus*). N.P: Marineret (Fornells); A.M.: Bruixa, au de temporal, vinjolita marina, bruixeta; Mall.: Noneta; C.: Ocell de tempesta; Cast.: Paíño común (**9**).

9. Storm Petrel
(*Hydrobates pelagicus*)

A curious little bird from all points of view. Small and mysterious, very little is known about it. It is quite difficult to observe since it is scarce and of pelagic habits, in fact only at night during breeding season do they come close to shore (April/August). It was first confirmed on the island in spring of 91 when a small breeding community of only 10 pairs were found on a small rocky islet. However not enough information has yet been collected for a positive judgement. Its favorite food is the plankton which floats on the sea after storms (maybe this is where the name originates) and it eats small fish on the water surface. Like cory's shearwater (belongs to the same family) it breeds on the cliffs near the sea and lays one single egg that is incubated 40 days by both parents. This bird is much more common on the other Balearic Islands than on Minorca.

Leach's Petrel (*Oceanodroma leucorrhoa*). N.P.: Petrell cuaforcat; A.M.: Bruixeta coaforcada, vinjolita marina grossa; Mall.: Noneta grossa; C.: Petrell cuaforcat; Cast: Paíño de Leach.

It is a rare bird in the Mediterranean. In Minorca there is only reference to one capture that dates back to July 1926 about 80 kms off the northwest coast.

ORDER PELECANIFORMES

FAMILY SULIDAE

Gannet (*Sula Bassana*). N.P.: Mascarell; A.M.: Àliga marina; Mall: Soteler; C.: Mascarell; Cast.: Alcatraz **(10)**.

A large and beautiful sea bird, of distinguished shape and flight. In Minorca it is scarce and irregular during winter. There aren't many observations taken down, but definitely every year we get visitors from the larger breeding colonies from the British isles and similar latitudes (two recoveries of this species have occurred here in the Balearics of birds originally ringed in the U.K.).

One must be very patient to watch this bird,

10. Gannet
(*Sula bassana*)

and be provided with a telescope or a pair of good binoculars, and a great deal of good luck... but once seen never forgotten due to its spectacular dive and the way it submerges in order to fish.

FAMILY PHALACROCORACIDAE

Cormorant (*Phalacrocorax carbo*). N.P.: Corb marí gros; A.M.: Corb marí continental, cagaire gros; Mall.: Corpetassa; C.: Corb marí gros; Cast.: Cormorán grande; **(11)** (Photos 3 and 34).

Large winter visitor similar to the shag, but with different habits.

In Minorca they start arriving in September, and it is December when the larger number of specimens is concentrated; they start leaving in February-March, but some specimens can be seen well into April.

11. Cormorant
(Phalacrocorax carbo)

In Minorca they mostly concentrate at S'Albufera, and since 1972 numbers have increased due to protection measures taken in countries of origin. At present there are about 350 winter residents.

During the daytime they rest inactive perched on the well-known rocky islet "des Cagaires" and on others close by (Photo 3).

At sundown groups gradually head for the western coast to spend the night. (from Es Grau beach they can be seen in the early evening).

A reduced number of specimens can be seen every winter in the Port of Maó, Salines d'Addaia, Tirant and sporadically in migration periods all over the Minorcan coast line. In Fornells, during the years when the fish-farm was fully functioning, cormorants were abundant causing controversy to the owners.

Our visitor the cormorant belongs to the continental subspecies (*Ph.C. sinensis*). From February onwards some specimens start to get their nuptial feathers.

The Minorcan winter visitors mainly came from the Holland, Denmark and Germany. This information, once more, has been obtained by ringing techniques.

The main food source is fish captured underwater with their bill.

Balearic Shag (*Phalacrocorax aristotelis*). N.P.: Corb marí; A.M.: Cagaire; Mall.: Corb marí; C.: Corb marí emplomallat; Cast.: Cormorán moñudo **(12)** (Photo 2).

A coastal sea bird very common in Minorca, it spends most of its life swimming, fishing and perching on reefs, rocks, buoys, piers, etc.

They can be seen all round the Minorcan coastline.

With a bit of luck, when snorkeling near the shore, one can see the young tame ones following a prey.

The reproduction period is December-January through April, although dates may change from one year to the next. Breeding in colonies on cliffs or rocky islets all round the island, the major concentration is towards the northwest.

12. Balearic Shag
(Phalacrocorax aristotelis)

The nest, round and made of twigs; can reach large proportions if used various seasons. Normally 3 eggs are laid and incubated by both parents for 30-31 days.

Fish is the base of their diet, they catch it with the bill after chasing their prey at a fast speed.

Minorcan shags are rather sedentary with few recoveries of ringed specimens, and always very near to the ringing points (2 or 3 specimens ringed in Majorca were found here). One specimen ringed in Majorca was recovered in the south of France and a Shag ringed in Corsica was found in Cabrera. The reproductive population of the island is estimated at about 300/400 pairs.

ORDER CICONIIFORMES

FAMILY ARDEIDAE

Bittern (*Botaurus stellaris*). N.P.: Bitó (comú); A.M.: Vendebou, veu de bou; Mall: Bitó, queca; C.: Bitó comú; Cast.: Avetoro común **(13)**.

This beautiful bird of the same family as the herons had become scarce during the last few decades in and around the European breeding areas. This was due to various factors, but at present it seems to be slowly recuperating.

13. Bittern
(Botaurus stellaris)

In Majorca some pairs have resettled in S'Albufera de Muro, where it had vanished as a breeder.

In Minorca it can be considered a scarce passage bird. In the last 12 years it has been observed on at least 6 occasions, always during spring.

Anyway, this Bittern has discreet and withdrawn habits, no doubt an important factor regarding the likelihood of its sighting or observation.

The most favorable watching locations are: Es Prat de S'Albufera, Son Bou and Son Saura North.

Little Bittern (*Ixobrychus minutus*). N.P.: Suís; Mall: Suís; C: Martinet menut; Cast: Avetorillo **(14)**.

The little bittern, as its name well indicates, is small in size, like a pigeon, and has striking black and pinkish feathers. Rare and difficult to see in Minorca. Observations registered during the last 20 years show that this bird can be seen during migration periods, especially in springtime and on a regular basis.

The best areas to watch Little bittern are reed-beds: S'Albufera, Son Bou, Son Saura North. In Son Bou it has been observed in summer but its breeding on the island has not been confirmed; this could be possible, even on an irregular basis. But as time goes by it

From left to right and top to bottom:
1.- Little Grebe (*Tachybaptus ruficollis*), with Summer plumage (Photo R.V.)
2.- Balearic Shag (*Phalacrocorax aristotelis*), immature specimen (Photo R.V.)
3.- Cormorants (*Phalacrocorax carbo*) at the Cagaires islet (S'Albufera) (Photo R.V.)
4.- Cory's Shearwater (*Calonectris diomedea*), taking flight in open sea (Photo Fèlix de Pablo).
5.- Little Egret (*Egretta garzetta*) (Photo F.P.)

14. Little Bittern *(Ixobrychus minutus)*   15. Night Heron *(Nycticorax nycticorax)*

becomes unlikely due to the degradation process of these favourable areas.

But they do breed in Majorca's Natural Park S'Albufera. Due to the withdrawn and discreet habits of this bird, the few observations recorded reflect only a very small percentage of the true number.

Curiously, a recovery of a little bittern ringed in Minorca in September 1956 occurred in Italy.

Night Heron *(Nycticorax nycticorax)*. N.P.: Orval; A.M.: Suís cendrós; Mall.: Orval; C.: Martinet de nit; Cast: Martinete **(15)**.

This species is relatively common on the island during migration periods and occasionally in summer, but it does not breed here. Oddly enough this bird is found in forest boundaries perched on tall trees surrounding wetlands. They normally travel in flocks of a fairly

---

From left to right and top to bottom:
6.- Booted Eagle *(Hieraetus pennatus)* on its nest (Photo R.V.)
7.- Grey Heron *(Ardea cinerea)* (Photo R.V.)
8.- Red Kite *(Milvus milvus)* (Photo R.V.)
9.- Stone Curlew *(Burhinus oedicnemus)* (Photo R.V.)
10.- Kestrel *(Falco tinnunculus)*, a male arriving at nest, where three grown chickens wait (Photo R.V)
11.- Mallard *(Anas platyrhynchos)*, male and female (Photo R.V.)

reduced size. At night when in flight they make a peeping hoarse "kwok" sound. In 1991 they re-established as breeders at the Natural Park of S'Albufera d'Alcúdia in Majorca, where seemingly they had become extinct.

Squacco Heron (*Ardeola ralloides*). N.P.: Toret; A.M.: Garsa monyuda; Mall: Toret; C.: Martinet ros; Cast.: Garcilla cangrejera **(16)**.

16. Squacco Heron *(Ardeola Ralloides)*

A small and beautiful heron, it is generally of solitary habits. Relatively frequent on the island during migration periods, especially spring (April-May) but rarely seen in summer and fall.

Most observations recalled in Minorca correspond to solitary individuals around wetlands (rather unnoticed). It has been seen around the areas of S'Albufera, Salines and Port of Fornells. These areas being more frequented by ornithologists, record the highest number of specimens of this species, however they have been seen around the Port of Maó along the streams of Sant Joan, in Cala Mesquida's wetlands etc..

Occasional summer observations have been made, yet seemingly are not related to breeding on the island.

Cattle Egret (*Bubulcus ibis*). N.P.: Esplugabous; A.M.: Garsa blanca; Mall. and C.: Esplugabous; Cast.: Garcilla bueyera **(17)**.

This curious little egret is becoming more and more common during wintertime due to the fact that this species is going through an expansion process all round southern Europe. In just over 30 years, breeding colonies have been established all over Spain and the south of France.

In Majorca it can be observed all year round, in the Natural Parc of S'Albufera, where in 1991 a breeding attempt was observed that will probably consolidate in the near future.

17. Cattle Egret *(Bubulcus ibis)*   18. Little Egret *(Egretta garzetta)*

In Minorca observations are, for the time being, restricted to migration and winter periods, only affecting solitary specimens or small groups.

The cattle egret's image is always associated to cattle (in Minorca mainly bovine) since their diet is based on cow parasites and related insects. This is the reason why one often finds them perched on or around cows, horses or in fields and meadows frequented by these animals such as the meadows of Son Bou or in Es Prat de S'Albufera ("Es Pla de Favaritx") and lately they have also been observed around the wetlands of Lluriac and nearby areas.

Two cattle egrets originally ringed in Huelva have been found in the Balearic Islands.

Little Egret *(Egretta garzetta)*. N.P.: Agró blanc; A.M.: Agronet blanc, garsa blanca; Mall.: Agró blanc; C.: Martinet blanc; Cast.: Garceta común. **(18)** (Photo 5).

Common species but found in small numbers all year[1] round all over Minorcan wetlands, especially in S'Albufera as it provides most favourable conditions for this bird. During migration it is more frequent and solitary individuals or groups can be observed along the Minorcan coastline, especially near beaches with small wetlands such as Algaiarens, Tre'elúger, Tirant, Cala Galdana etc...

---

[1] Specimens observed in summer are non-breeding individuals.

Confident and elegant, the shape of the Little Egret is always a pleasure for the bird watcher.

It is important not to confuse it from a distance with the cattle egret or with the squacco heron as in flight it appears all white. Neither must it be mistaken for the Great White Heron (*Egretta alba*) although this is a rare and occasional visitor.

During spring and summer quite a lot of specimens can be observed with nuptial feathers on the back of their heads. Their main source of nourishment are small fish and other vertebrates and invertebrate aquatic creatures, which they capture waiting patiently in quiet waters and by shooting their head and neck suddenly towards the prey.

Great White Egret (*Egretta alba*). N.P.: Agró blanc gros; Mall.: Agró blanc gros; C.: Agró blanc; Cast.: Garceta grande.

This species is rare and vagrant, observed on few occasions during winter. They stay only for a few weeks on the island in the S'Albufera marshlands, where it has most often been watched. Although it has a cosmopolitan distribution is quite rare now in Europe and in the Balearic Islands.

Grey Heron (*Ardea cinerea*). N.P.: Agró gris; A.M.: Agró; Garsa grisa, agró o garsa reial; Mall.: Agró; C.: Bernat pescaire; Cast.: Garza real **(19)** (Photo 7).

This heron is present all year round on the island, but it is more abundant during migration periods. Quite a few specimens use the island for winter quarters, and others are summer visitors, but there is no proof of it breeding here. Since 1990 there are a few breeding pairs in the Natural Park of S'Albufera de Mallorca.

We can find it in S'Albufera des Grau, Salines, Port Addaia, Fornells and in marshlands such as Son Bou and during migration in any small wetland and coastal areas. Sometimes they may even venture off to ponds or abandoned pools to rest or eat, if there are fish and frogs.

The Grey heron's flight is slow and majestic, alternating dense flaps with gliding, emitting at the same time a harsh "crag" similar to crows. Most visitors come from central and eastern Europe. So far a minimum of 10 birds ringed on the Balearics have been controlled: 4 in Poland, 2 in France, 1 in Austria 1 in Switzerland, 1 in Germany, 1 in Russia.

19. Grey Heron *(Ardea Cinerea)*   20. Purple Heron *(Ardea purpurea)*

Purple Heron *(Ardea purpurea)*. N.P.: Agró roig; A.M.: Garsa rotja; Mall + C.: Agró roig; Cast.: Garza imperial (20).

A beautifully feathered heron that appears on the island in small numbers during migration from March to June and August to September.

It is slightly smaller than the grey heron and from a distance can be mistaken, especially under poor lighting. Its customs and eating habits are similar to the Grey heron although the Purple heron prefers to hide around reed-bed areas.

Just a few specimens spend summers in Minorca. S'Albufera or Son Bou marshes are the most favourable habitats for this species but they do not breed here. Maybe a small group bred here in the past as still occurs in S'Albufera d'Alcúdia, but there is no valid information available.

During migration especially solitary specimens can be found in any wet area.

8 recoveries of ringed Purple herons have taken place in the Balearics: 3 from France, 2 Holland, 2 Switzerland, 1 ringed in Toledo. One chick ringed in Majorca was found dead 2 months later in Girona.

FAMILY CICONIIDAE

White Stork (*Ciconia ciconia*). N.P. + Mall + Cat.: Cigonya blanca; A.M.: Cigonya; Cast.: Cigüeña blanca.

The mythical White Stork, so common on mainland Spain, only presents itself on the island as an accidental migrant diverted from its usual migratory routes, although observations have been recorded most years during March-May, August-October and erratic appearances.

On mainland Spain it is a rather studied species by ornithologists, and it is now recovering from the sharp fall occurred during the 50s, 60s and 70s.

The White stork has been the object of severe protection and scientific ringing campaigns, which are now producing results. On the islands at least 6 ringed birds have been observed: 3 from Germany, 1 from Czechoslovakia, 1 from Switzerland and 1 from Badajoz.

Black Stork (*Ciconia nigra*). N.P.: Cigonya negra; Mall.: Cigonya negra; C.: Cigonya negra; Cast.: Cigüeña negra.

Scarce, less known than the previous species. The Black Stork is an accidental migrator rather rare in Minorca. Only four observations have been recorded during the last ten years, which in all cases have been solitary specimens.

FAMILY THRESKIORNITIDAE

Glossy Ibis (*Plegadis falcinellus*). N.P. + Mall.: Ibis negre; A.M.: Ibis rotget; C.: Capó reial; Cast.: Morito.

This is also a rather rare accidental migrant on the island, only observed on 3 occasions during the last 10 years. Probably originating from southwest Europe, where the closest breeding areas are based.

Spoonbill (*Platalea leucorodia*). N.P. + Mall + C.: Bec-planer; Cast.: Espátula.

This is another example of an accidental visitor. The few observations registered on solitary specimens have been near Addaia, S'Albufera, and the Port of Fornells where they usually spend a few weeks. A bird originally ringed in Holland was recovered in Majorca.

ORDER PHOENICOPTERIFORMES

FAMILY PHOENICOPTERIDAE

Greater Flamingo (*Phoenicopterus ruber*). N.P. + Mall.: Flamenc; C.: Flamenc; Àlic roig; Cast.: Flamenco (photo 34).

The Greater flamingo is a vagrant that occasionally spends a few weeks on the island during migration or in winter. During the winter of 94/95 a group consisting of 12 young specimens were spotted in Addaia. The most popular areas in Minorca for flamingos are S'Albufera, Port of Fornells and Addaia. Most probably all the specimens observed in Minorca came from Camargue (South of France) where they are abundant breeders. 3 birds ringed there have been sited in our islands (2 in Majorca and one in Minorca).

ORDER ANSERIFORMES

FAMILY ANATIDAE

Mute Swan (*Cygnus olor*). N.P. + Mall + C.: Cigne mut; Cast.: Cisne vulgar.

This species had not been recorded on the island until 1989, when during fall 8 rather tame specimens arrived which could be observed from the water processing plant at Es Migjorn Gran to Addaia and Fornells. Four of these birds remained until February 1990. One of them was sent to the "Son Reus" birds rehabilitation center in Majorca, where it died soon after. It had been ringed in Hungary 4 months before.

Whooper Swan (*Cygnus cygnus*). N.P. + Mall + C.: Cigne cantaire; Cast.: Cisne cantor.

There is only reference to one capture in December 1939 at Lluriac, this swan was with three others and probably belonged to the same species; unfortunately they were also captured.

Bewick's Swan (*Cygnus columbianus/bewickii*). N.P.+ Mall + C.: Cigne petit; Cast.: Cisne chico.

There is only one known reference of this species and it is a stuffed specimen kept at the Maó Ateneu. It seems like this specimen was captured before 1911.

From the above information we can establish that the presence of swans on the island are exceptional situations related to the extremely cold winters that occasionally affect the European continent.

Bean Goose (*Anser fabalis*). N.P. + Mall.: Oca de camp; A.M.: Oca salvatge; C.: Oca pradenca; Cast.: Ansar campestre.

During the past 20 years no confirmed observations have been made. However, this bird can easily go unnoticed among other species of geese. Mainland Spain is the winter quarters of a small north European breeding population.

Greylag Goose (*Anser anser*). N.P.: Oca comuna; Mall.: Oca salvatge; C.: Oca vulgar; A.M.: Oca salvatge, oca rossa; Cast.: Ansar común. **(21)**.

21. Greylag Goose *(Anser anser)*

This species can be observed from mid November to February around S'Albufera des Grau. Sporadically it can also be seen at other locations such as: Lluriac, Addaia and Prat de Son Bou. The number of yearly winter visitors is of about 20 specimens. The Greylag g. is the species from which many domestic geese originate. Feeding habits are essentially vegetarian, consuming a wide range of plants.

Barnacle Goose (*Branta Leucopsis*). N.P. + Mall + C.: Oca de galta blanca; Cast.: Barnacla cariblanca.

Exceptional to the island, there is only one recorded observation in Jan'85 around Cavalleria, which arrived due to the cold wave in northern Europe.

Shelduck (*Tadorna tadorna*). N.P.: Àneda blanca; A.M.: Àneda muda; Mall.: Ànnera blanca; C.: Ànec Blanc; Cast.: Tarro blanco.

Until recent years this was considered a scarce and irregular winter visitor. Presently it seems that this bird is going through an expansion phase and observations have become more regular. In fact it has sporadically nested in Majorca and Ibiza. The best locations to watch them are the Salinas and Port of Addaia and Fornells, on a smaller scale at S'Albufera and Son Bou.

Wigeon (*Anas penelope*). N.P.: Xiulaire; A.M.: Àneda xiuladora; Mall.: Siulador; C.: Ànec xiulador, Ànnera xiuladora; Cast.: Ánade silbón **(22)**.

Regular winter visitor, abundant in S'Albufera, and, depending on the seasonal rainfall, the areas of Lluriac, Addaia, Morella, Son Saura and Son Bou.

During migration pe-riôds it can be found in smaller wetlands. It is important to outline that generally aquatic birds, and above all ducks, tend to change their lo-

22. Wigeon (*Anas penelope*)

cation depending on solitude, food conditions etc... Essentially this explains that one day there might be a large concentration of ducks in Morella or Addaia and the following day not a single one to be seen.

S'Albufera, due to its size and food resources, welcomes a larger proportion of aquatic winter visitors. Other wetlands, although they shelter a smaller percentage, also act as alternative areas in the case of dangerous or risky situations such as abundance of hunters, too many curious and noisy visitors, presence of fishing boats).

Another frequent phenomenon is the concentration of certain species which can be seen in coastal areas, such as mallards or wigeons, which either perch there due to the above reasons or for resting purposes. This can normally be seen between Es Grau and Colom island or between Tirant and Cavalleria.

Wigeons are regularly on the island from the beginning of September to the end of April and occasionally in May. The highest density is during Dec. and Jan.

The census taken during the last 20 years accounts for a winter population of approximately 150 specimens.

Mandarin Duck (*Aix galericulata*). N.P.: Àneda mandarina; Mall.: Ànnera mandarina; C.: Ànec mandarí; Cast.: Pato Mandarín.

Originating in China, it was introduced to some areas of Europe (especially England) as a decorative bird. Escaped specimens have established themselves in the wilderness of some countries.

During the last couple of years a tame female has been observed at the mouth of Cala En Porter's stream, accompanied by domestic ducks which undoubtedly had escaped from somewhere.

Gadwall (*Anas strepera*). N.P.: Àneda griseta; A.M.: Àneda grisa, siulet; Mall.: Ànnera griseta; C.: Ànec griset; Cast.: Ánade friso. ›

A scarce regular winter visitor, from December to March. There are a few observations in October and November, which are probably incidental.

Observation spots in order of importance are: S'Albufera, Lluriac, Morella, Salines d'Addaia, Son Bou.

Like the wigeon, the Gadwall is a duck that feeds on fresh water vegetation.

The average winter census is estimated around 15 specimens, with yearly fluctuations (minimum 0, maximum 28).

Teal (*Anas crecca*) N.P.: Anedó; A.M.: Anneró; Mall.: Sel.la rossa; C.: Xarxet; Cast.: Cerceta común **(23)**.

This small duck is a regular winter visitor that can be observed during migration periods (mid-August to March).

The most favourable habitat is S'Albufera and it can also be spotted around

23. Teal *(Anas crecca)*

Lluriac, Morella, Addaia, Son Saura North, Son Bou, Salines de Fornells and other small wetlands on the island. It often rests at sea.

During December and January up to 324 specimens have been censed; the average figure being around 100 winter visitors, with strong year to year fluctuations.

Most teals come from the south of Europe, since this has been proved with the 9 retrieved teals ringed in France.

Mallard (*Anas platyrhynchos*). N.P.: Coll-blau; A.M.: Coll-verd, Àneda or Ànnera rossa o Salvatge; Mall.: Coll-blau, capblau; Cat: Ànec collverd; Cast.: Ánade real **(24)** Photo 11.

24. Mallard *(Anas platyrhynchos)*

The only duck species that breeds in Minorca on a regular basis is the Mallard, therefore it is the most commonly known by farmers and hunters. In winter and during migration periods it is more abundant due to the arrival of European migrants.

All domestic ducks descend from the Mallard.

The breeding areas in order of importance are: S'Albufera des Grau, Prat de Son Bou, Tirant-Lluriac, Addaia, Algaiarens, Sa Mesquida etc... It is possible that they might nest in Son Saura North and South, Morella, Prat de Cala En Porter, Salines de Fornells and Algendar, Trebalúger, Binimel·là etc. In fact nests have been found near streams and even in fields some distance away from water. The reproductive population around S'Albufera is estimated to be about 40/50 pairs.

From March to June female Mallards can be seen followed by their young chicks (3 to 10, since lay is between 9/13 eggs). The average winter community is of approximately 500 specimens.

So far within the Balearic Islands only one ringed Mallard has been retrieved, it was originally from France.

Pintail (*Anas acuta*). N.P.: Coer; A.M.: Àneda o ànnera amb coa; Mall: Coer; C.: Ànec cuallarg; Cast.: Ánade rabudo **(25)**.

25. Pintail *(Anas acuta)*

Scarce but regular winter visitor from September to April. Best area for watching is S'Albufera followed by Addaia.

The average census (Dec-Jan) is estimated at about 10 specimens. No doubt that this is one of the most beautiful ducks visiting the island.

Garganey *(Anas querquedula)*. N.P.: Anedó blanc; A.M.: Anedó o anneró de celles blanques; C.: Xarrasclet; Mall.: Sel·la blanca; Cast.: Cerceta carretona.

Migrator, can be observed from February to April, exceptionally till June. During fall it is more scarce and irregular. On numbered occasions it has been observed August and September. Found in wetlands all over the island although always in reduced groups spending only short periods here. The best watching spot is S'Albufera. A bird ringed in Holland was retrieved in Majorca.

Shoveler *(Anas clypeata)*. N.P.: Cullerot; A.M.: Ànnera o àneda de bec planer; Mall.: Cullerot; C: Ànec cullerot; Cast.: Pato cuchara. **(26)**.

Regular migrator and winter visitor in small numbers. Can be observed from Sep-tember to May, but between November and February it is more abundant. S'Albufera is their favorite spot, followed by Lluriac. It is more irregular around

26. Shoveler *(Anas clypeata)*

Addaia, Salines and Fornells, Morella, Son Bou and Son Saura.

With its interesting beak it sieves tiny seeds and animals from water. The winter census is under 100 specimens. In Majorca a Shoveler ringed in Czechoslovakia was retrieved.

Blue-winged Teal (*Anas discors*). N.P.: Anedó alablau; C.: Xarxet alablau; Cast.: Cerceta aliazul.

This is an american species vagrant all round Europe. There is one observation of a male specimen who stayed in S'Albufera for 2 weeks in January 1990.

Red-crested Pochard (*Netta rufina*). N.P.: Àneda de bec vermell; Mall.: Bec vermell; C.: Xibec, ànec de bec vermell, Cast.: Pato colorado.

Exceptional visitor. Observation of a pair was recorded between Feb. 77 and May 78 at S'Albufera. Sporadic visits are not impossible since it breeds on the eastern coast of mainland Spain and the south of France. It has recently been re-introduced to S'Albufera d'Alcúdia, Majorca, and some pairs already breed wild.

Pochard (*Aythya ferina*). N.P.: Rabassot; A.M.: Àneda o ànnera de cap vermell; Mall.: Moretó; C.: Morell cap-roig; Cast.: Porrón comú **(27)**.

27. Pochard *(Aythya ferina)*

Amongst the Minorcans there is a popular expression «Dormir com un rabasot» = «To sleep like a pochard». And no doubt that to sleep is one of the most characteristic habits of this duck; it is very abundant on the island, spends all day sleeping and feeds at nighttime.

It is common as a winter visitor and migrant, although summer observations have been recorded of solitary specimens or small non-breeding groups, these being occasional summer visitors or either early or late migrants.

The winter population stabilizes towards the end of November till mid February.

S'Albufera welcomes about 80%, and the rest, depending on rainfall, spread out around Morella, Lluriac, Addaia, Salines Port of Fornells and Son Bou. In good years the census has reached figures up to 1400 specimens while during dry and warm winters the figure decreases to 100-150. Food: aquatic plants, also small mollusks and crustaceans.

Tufted Duck (*Aythya fuligula*). N.P.: Rabassot de cresta; A.M.: Àneda de cresta o peixetera, rabassot caraputxí; Mall.: Moretó de puput; C.: Morell de plomall; Cas.: Porrón moñudo.

Regular winter visitor (in small numbers). It is a regular around S'Albufera from November to February, and an occasional visitor to other wetlands.

During migration it has been seen in many areas. Some observations in summer have been recorded, and considered occasional. The general prevailing census during the past 20 winters is of 15 specimens.

Scaup (*Aythya marila*). N.P.: Rabassot cabussó; A.M.: Rabassot bord; Mall.: Moretó cabussó; C.: Morell buixot, Cast.: Porrón bastardo.

Exceptional winter visitor, rather few observations registered in S'Albufera during December and January.

Due to the fact that the Scaup is a sea bird, some specimens can go unnoticed around ports and coastal areas when visiting the island. The Scaup originates in northern Europe and only a few manage to reach the Mediterranean during winter.

Ferruginous Duck (*Aythya nyroca*). N.P.: Rabassot menut; A.M.: Rabassotet, anneró o anedó; Mall.: Parda; C.: Morell xocolater; Cast.: Porrón pardo.

Rare, vagrant, irregular winter visitor, during the last decades this species has suffered a regression regarding distribution areas. They have been observed mostly at S'Albufera.

Goldeneye (*Bucephala clangula*). N.P.: Rabassot d'ulls grocs; C.: Morell d'ulls grocs; Cast.: Porrón osculado.

Only one observation registered at the Port of Maó, a solitary specimen in 1987 which stayed from January to early February.

Eider (*Somateria mollissima*). N.P. + Mall + C.: Eider, Cast.: Eider común.

Only one registration at the Port of Maó in January 88. Like previous species, the Eider is a scarce winter visitor to the Mediterranean.

Common Scoter (*Melanitta nigra*). N.P.: Àneda negreta; A.M.: Àneda negra; Mall.: Negreta; C.: Ànec negre; Cast.: Negrón Común.

The only registered observation took place in Addaia in November 74; this bird mainly spends winters on the Atlantic coast and is rare around the Mediterranean. Being mainly a sea bird it can easily go by unnoticed.

Velvet Scoter (*Melanitta fusca*). N.P.: Àneda fosca; Mall.: Ànnera fosca; C.: Ànec fosc; Cast.: Negrón especulado.

Only one observation recorded, and this was in the Port of Maó, between January and March 85. Of similar behaviors and distribution areas as the common Scoter, yet it is even less frequent around Mediterranean areas.

Red-breasted Merganser (*Mergus serrator*). N.P.: Àneda peixetera; A.M.: Xerret; Mall.: Ànnera peixetera; C.: Bec de serra mitjà; Cast.: Serreta mediana.

Rare and irregular winter visitor. Observations have been quoted in the following areas: Port of Maó, Port of Fornells, Port of Ciutadella and Port of Addaia.

In Majorca it is considered a scarce winter visitor, so it is possible that some years it goes by unnoticed here in Minorca.

Even less frequent as winter visitors are the Smew and Goosander of which we only have 2 very old and doubtful registrations, but again, they possibly go by unnoticed.

ORDER ACCIPITRIFORMES

FAMILY ACCIPITRIDAE

Honey Buzzard (*Pernis apivorus*). N.P.: Falcó vesper; A.M.: Falcó de muntanya; Mall.: Falcó vesper; C.: Aligot vesper, falcó vesper; Cast.: Halcón abejero.

A beautiful bird of prey, it can be observed during spring, and less often in fall, on migration route. The best time is May followed by June and April.

In fall it is more rare, and has only been observed in September and October.

It is normally seen in groups, sometimes quite large ones, on migratory routes gliding both inland and along the coastline when leaving the island.

In fact, often they don't even stopover; very few observations have been made of Honey buzzards staying overnight, if they do so, it is at the top of a very high tree.

Specimens observed around the Balearics represent a very small percentage of all Honey buzzards that travel from Europe to Africa and vice versa during migration periods, since their gliding abilities need thermal air currents which are not generated over the sea. Most Honey buzzards cross over strategic points where the sea crossing is geographically reduced to a minimum, hence Gibraltar, where over 150.000 specimens cross over every year.

This bird receives its name, as implied (also in other mentioned languages), from its eating habits which are mainly wasp larvae which it digs out of nests in the ground.

Black Kite (*Milvus migrans*). N.P. and C.: Milà negre; Mall.: Milana negra; Cast.: Milano negro.

It is a scarce migrant. There are some winter observations which indicate it is an irregular winter visitor. There are observations of young specimens during July and August, possibly first migrants or during nest leaving dispersion. Like the species above mentioned, very few migrate over the sea.

Red kite (*Milvus milvus*). N.P.: Milà; A.M.: Milà poller; Milà forcany, Forcany; Mall.: Milana reial; C.: Milà reial; Cast.: Milano real **(28)** (Photo 8).

The Red Kite is a local breeder and a bird of prey. Until recently it was very common and abundant on the island, to such a degree that G.O.B used the shape of the Red Kite to illustrate the logo of their entity.

From left to right and top to bottom:

12.- Kentish Plover (*Charadrius alexandrinus*) male. (Photo R.V.)

13.- Black-winged Stilt (*Himantopus himantopus*) (Photo R.V.)

14.- Black-tailed Godwit (*Limosa limosa*) (Photo F.P.)

15.- Yellow-legged Gull (*Larus cachinnans*): 3 grown up chicks near a breeding colony (Photo R.V).

28. Red kite *(Milvus milvus)*

Only 10 years ago the estimated reproductive population was of 150 pairs, making it the highest density in the whole of its distribution area (mainly European). On the continent it has suffered a strong regression and has become extinct in some areas. At present there are under 50 breeding pairs in Minorca and this figure is really worrying. The reasons for this dramatic drop in numbers are at present under study, but the following points seem to stand out:

1) The use and abuse of poison to kill cats, dogs, ravens and other animals (considered as menaces to both professional and amateur farmers). 2) Changes in traditional farming. 3) Abuse of chemical products. 4) Decrease of potential prey, such as rabbits. 5) Competition with other species such as gulls. 6) Destruction of habitats and breeding places. 7) Direct hunting etc..

The Administration is expected to take urgent measures in order to avoid this continuous decrease of population and recover or at least stabilize the population numbers.

The Red Kites are scavenger birds that collect and eat corpses of any dead animal and only occasionally hunt small birds, mammals, reptiles etc..

From December to February, the nuptial flights are interesting to watch (always near the nest points). From February to March they rebuild the nest, which can become very large over the years. Nests

From up to down:
16.- Yellow legged Gull *(Larus cachinnans)* Adult specimen. (Photo R.V.)
17.- Black headed Gull *(Larus ridibundus)* (Photo R.V.)
18.- Audouin's Gull *(Larus audouinii)* (Photo F.P.)

are normally built on top of high trees, and occasionally on cliffs. They lay between 2 and 3 eggs that are incubated 28-30 days.

During fall and winter they concentrate in large groups around forest areas (to sleep together) such as La Vall. La Vall is the area where this species is most abundant and stable at present.

Minorcan Kites are basically sedentary, year-round residents, although there are some winter and migratory visitors. This fact is known due to the recovery of ringed birds. There is hardly any information about juvenile dispersion, but it is suspected that some young Red Kites leave the island upon their emancipation.

Egyptian Vulture (*Neophron percnopterus*). N.P.: Miloca; A.M.: Miloca, arpella, arpellot, àguila d'Altoro, Milà blanc; Mall.: Moixeta voltonera; C.: Aufrany; Cast.: Alimoche (**29**).

The only vulture that breeds on the island, in fact here it probably reaches the highest density of all distribution areas.

The breeding resident population is of about 40 pairs. The other Egyptian Vultures in Europe migrate to Africa in winter.

They build their nests in small clefts or caves. They lay 2 eggs which are incubated 42 days by both

29. Egyptian Vulture *(Neophron percnopterus)*

parents. This normally takes place in April. The eggshell removal occurs during May or June, and only one chick manages to survive. Right till end of August or beginning of September, the brown-feathered chick can be seen in or around the nest.

Like all other birds of prey, the Egyptian Vulture gets very sensitive when breeding and one has to make sure not to bother them during this period.

Like the kites, during autumn and winter they concentrate in large numbers to sleep.

As scavengers, these vultures live off carrion (cows, lambs, rabbits etc.) and are an important sanitary contribution within nature. Their diet is completed with insects such as beatles and some plants.

They can be observed almost anywhere on the island, in pairs or small groups, but observations tend to be more successful near breeding areas such as ravines, inland or sea cliffs. The population on the island seems to be stable, although dead specimens have been found near rubbish dumps and other spots during the last few years.

During migration a few outsider specimens stop over. But there is no information regarding the juvenile dispersion.

Black Vulture (*Aegypius monachus*). N.P.+ Mall + C.: Voltor negre; A.M.: Arpellot; Cast.: Buitre negro.

It is is the largest bird in Europe. There is a small community in the "Serra de Tramuntana", Majorca, which at present is going through a recuperation program since it was about to become extinct.

A specimen ringed in Majorca was found drowned on the northwest coast of Ciutadella.

The few observations recorded on the island, no doubt are of specimens based in Majorca.

Short-toed Eagle (*Circaetus gallicus*). N.P. + C.: Àguila marcenca; Mall.: Àguila culebrera; Cast.: Àguila culebrera.

Possible regular visitor during migration although observations haven't been made every year. It can be observed from March to July, and May is the month with most registrations. It is scarce in autumn. Its favorite food are reptiles and especially snakes. It breeds in most European countries and migrates to Africa for the winter.

Marsh Harrier (*Circus aeruginosus*). N.P.: Arpella; A.M.: Arpella d'aigua; Mall + Cat.: Arpella; Cast.: Aguilucho lagunero (**30**).

A medium-sized bird of prey, it is present on the island during migration and winter. The winter residents, no more than 10 members, are mainly based in S'Albufera and Son Bou and irregularly at Lluriac, Son Saura North and Morella.

During migration periods (March to May and September to October), solitary specimens or small groups can be observed around almost any wetlands, even in open fields or coastal areas, acting as departure platforms for their forthcoming migration route.

30. Marsh Harrier *(Circus aeruginosus)*

Previous authors considered the Marsh Harrier a local resident, but no exact references of nesting were ever mentioned. We think that sporadically a pair could have bred in favorable conditions in reed-beds such as at Son Bou, Son Saura north or S'Albufera. In 1982 there was an unsuccessful attempt at nest building by a male. The rare summer observations are probably of vagrant specimens. Approximately 90% of Marsh Harriers observed are females or young birds. The rest are adult males.

Four ringed specimens (3 from Germany and 1 from Denmark) have been retrieved in the Balearic Islands.

Food: Frogs, reptiles, small mammals, birds (young ducks), insects, fish and even carrion.

Hen Harrier *(Circus cyaneus).* N.P.: Arpella d'albufera; A.M.: Arpella grisa; Mall.: Esparver d'albufera; C.: Arpella pàl·lida, esparver d'estany; Cast.: Aguilucho pálido.

Scarce winter resident and migrant, observations are taken from September to May/June.

Although easier to watch in wetlands, it can also be spotted on fields inland. It breeds in northern Europe and emigrates to the Mediterranean in winter.

Montagu's Harrier *(Circus pygargus).* N.P.: Arpella cendrosa o forastera; Mall.: Àguila d'albufera; C.: Esparver cendrós; Cast.: Aguilucho cenizo.

Scarce regular visitor during migration periods, with few observations. The lack of observations is probably due to the difficulty in telling it apart from the Hen harrier since they are very similar in appearance, especially the female specimen.

As of today the few veracious observations have been during March, April and September, in different areas. This Harrier spends summers in Europe and winters in central and south Africa.

Pallid Harrier (*Circus macrourus*). N.P.: Arpella russa; A.M.: Arpella cendrosa; Mall.: Arpella pàl·lida; C.: Arpella pàl·lida (russa); Cast.: Aguilucho papialbo.

It is a bird from eastern regions. Only one reference on the island in 1911, which is embalmed at the Ateneo Museum in Maó. This we can classify as exceptional visitor.

Sparrow Hawk (*Accipiter nisus*). N.P.: Falcó torder, A.M.: Falcó de tords, esparver torder, falcó petit, falcó reial; Mall.: Falcó torter; C.: Esparver; Cast.: Gavilán.

At present this species is considered a scarce migrant and winter visitor. But since its area of hunting activity is in forests and woodlands, it rarely flies in open spaces. Sporadically thrush hunters catch this bird with thrush nets.

There are a couple of vague quotations (1920 and 1975) regarding the breeding of this bird on the island but we consider this possibility almost non-existent.

Their favorite prey are small birds, the occasional small mammals and insects.

Buzzard (*Buteo buteo*). N.P.: Aligot; A.M.: Falcó reial, soter bord; Mall + C.: Aligot; Cast.: Ratonero común.

It is a winter resident, and a migrant, scarce summer visitor. Taking into account that this bird is a common resident of all areas surrounding the Balearics it is not surprising that 70 observations have been registered during the last 20 years, which are probably dispersed specimens.

Although two former ornithologists (Ponseti and Moll) considered this bird resident on the island, we feel this bird has never bred in Minorca, at least not on a regular basis.

Buzzards can be observed in many areas. They prefer to trap their prey from tree tops or high points rather than hovering.

Booted Eagle (*Hieraetus pennatus*). N.P.: Soter; A.M.: Espolsamates; esparver, esparver reial; Mall.: Esparver, C.: Àguila calçada; Cast.: Águila calzada **(31)** (Photo 6).

31. Booted Eagle *(Hieraetus pennatus))*

The Booted Eagle is in fact the only real eagle that lives on the island. It is a very active bird of prey that feeds on birds and mammals (until just a few years back rabbits were a very important part of their diet).

It is quite common to see these birds taking advantage of the strong thermal currents, especially around woodlands and near cliffs where their nests are built.

They lay 2 eggs, which are incubated for 30 days, but normally only one chick survives.

The population density is high, around 50 breeding pairs, possibly the highest density of all distribution areas. Here it is a resident whilst in all the other areas it is basically a migrator. There might be winter and migrator visitors, but this fact is little known. The young birds tend to stay on the island, which we know from the ringing.

Bonelli's Eagle *(Hieraetus fasciatus)*. N.P + Mall + C.: Àguila coabarrada; A.M.: Esparver; Cast.: Àguila perdicera

This is a rare or accidental visitor on the Balearics. Since 74 there have been no recorded observations. In Majorca seemingly this species became extinct as a breeder approximately 20 or 30 years ago.

Osprey *(Pandion haliaetus)*. N.P + Mall.: Àguila peixetera; A.M.: Foradadora d'aigua; Cat.: Àguila pescadora; Cast.: Aguila pescadora (32).

The Osprey is one of the most studied birds in Minorca. This is because of the great danger of it becoming extinct on the island. In 1978 G.O.B started a surveillance campaign in the breeding spots, in order to protect them from being disturbed during breeding periods. That year only two pairs survived, after a third couple joined up but didn't manage to produce any chicks. A hopeful sign of recuperation was observed in 1992 with the breeding of 4 pairs, and in 1993 five pairs bred successfully.

The decrease of this bird of prey in the Balearics (in Ibiza it hasn't bred for over 20 years) is due to various aspects: the most important one has been the destruction of small wetlands in order to build holiday complexes, disturbance in land or along coastal areas, and the direct hunting or capture of chicks from their nests.

32. Osprey *(Pandion haliaetus)*

The ornithologist from Ciutadella, Moll, in his book "Las aves de Menorca", 1957, points out 4 breeding couples on the south coast of the island, which must have disappeared during the late 60s, early 70s. At present they only breed in areas of difficult access along the north coast, and are hardly seen on the south coast.

At present Ospreys feed mostly at the Port of Fornells, S'Albufera and Port Addaia, however they can also be spotted flying over the coast or even inland on their daily trips.

During migration periods a few outsiders join the local population for a few days at a time. What is not certain is if the Ospreys seen in winter are the same breeding pairs or winter residents (which could be possible). In fact four Ospreys ringed in Scandinavia have been recovered here. The ringing of chicks born here will help us follow their movements in the future.

It is fascinating to watch their dives into the water, although a high percentage of them are unsuccessful. If they catch a fish they perch on a nearby point where they willingly devour it.

Lesser Kestrel *(Falco naumanni)*. N.P.: Xòric petit; A.M.: Rapinya; Mall + C.: Xoriguer petit; Cast.: Cernícalo primilla.

Very similar to the kestrel and difficult to tell apart unless it is by their distinctive songs and calls.

Due to the lack of information, it seems like this bird has become extinct as a breeder on the island (this is obviously supposing that it was a regular breeder from the start). The only accurate information is that at least two pairs bred in Es Barranc d'Algendar and Es Barranquet de Sant Joan, from the 70s to early 80s. Apart from this we do not have any reliable information. But it makes sense that some specimens visit the island during migration, and that with favourable conditions an occasional pair has started breeding, although the Mediterranean population has suffered from a great decrease during the last few years.

Kestrel (*Falco tinnunculus*), N.P: Xòric, Xuric; Mall + C.: Xoriguer; Cast.: Cernícalo vulgar **(33)** Photo 10

No doubt, this is the most abundant daytime bird of prey in Minorca. Kestrels find the island conditions very favourable to maintain large populations. During the last few years quite a few specimens have perished due to chemical products used on the fields and by direct hunting. In spite of this, the population density is kept at reasonable levels. We can observe Kestrels all over the island: inland, on the coast, near woodlands, in open fields, in villages and towns.

Its habit of hovering over its prey, looking down on it and its preference for open areas, makes it easily recognizable and a well-known bird. It often rests on

33. Kestrel (*Falco tinnunculus*)

telephone or electrical cables. Kestrels catch almost anything: small mammals, such as country mice, little birds, geckoes, lizards, small snakes and a whole range of insects.

During nest building, they are very noisy and their favorite spots are holes and little caves on cliff sides and rural buildings. Reproduction starts in March and lasts right up to August, they lay about five eggs which are mainly incubated by the female for about four weeks. The chicks grow quickly and before a month has passed they can be observed flying around the nests.

The Minorcan Kestrels are common residents, but during migration periods we get occasional visitors. 8 ringed birds from Europe have been retrieved on the islands (4 from Switzerland, 3 Germany, 1 France).

Red-footed Falcon (*Falco vespertinus*). N.P.: Falcó o xòric cama-roig; Mall.: Falcó cames-roges; C.: Falcó cama-roig, Cast.: Cernícalo patirrojo **(34)**.

This small exotic looking falcon can be observed during April, May and early June on migration route, yet in fall migration doesn't cross the island path.

34. Red-Footed Falcon
(*Falco vespertinus*)

Their distribution area is Western Europe and Asia, where they are summer residents, and they visit Africa during winters. Quite often they can be observed in groups, but solitary specimens can also be spotted flying low or perching on power/telephone cables searching for insects (mainly beatles and grasshoppers).

Merlin (*Falco columbarius*). N.P.: Esmerla; A.M.: Falconet; Mall. + C.: Esmerla; Cast.: Esmerejón.

A small falcon with a northern area of distribution, only arrives to this latitude during migration or winter. During the last 20 years only 4 or 5 observations have been registered, this could be considered as rare on the island.

Hobby (*Falco subbuteo*). N.P.: Falconet; A.M.: Xòric fosc; Mall.: Falconet; C.: Falcó mostatxut; Cast.: Alcotán.

Regular passage migrant, but a scarce and a solitary specimen. The best months to detect its presence are April, May and September. It is important not to mistake it with the pale form of Eleonora's Falcon. It can be observed almost anywhere but enjoys visiting wet areas where it catches large flying insects. It is very agile and fast and can even catch swifts on flight. Summer visitor all around Europe and northwestern Africa, spending winters in Central Africa.

Eleonora's Falcon (*Falco eleonorae*), N.P. and Mall.: Falcó marí; C.: Falcó de la reina; Cast.: Halcón de Eleonor.

Irregular visitor from April to October. Most observations are taken on the western coast of the island (around La Vall), basically corresponding to small groups or lone specimens coming from Majorca, Cabrera or their offshore rocky islands where there are abundant breeders. It is rather surprising that it breeds everywhere but in Minorca, in theory there is no reason for such an irregularity.

Like the hobby, Eleonora's Falcon, is agile and fast, seizing small birds and insects off coastal cliffs but it hunts inland too.

This species breeds and is based in the Mediterranean, North Africa and Canary Islands, spending winters in Madagascar.

Lanner (*Falco biarmicus*). N.P.: Falcó llaner; A.M.: Falcó roig; Mall and C.: Falcó Llaner; Cast.: Halcón Lanario o borní.

There are few observations registered, but it can easily go by unnoticed. In fact the closest breeding areas are in Italy and North Africa. In March 1971 a pair were hunted down, seemingly they were going to breed around La Mola of Maó; when the female was being prepared for embalmment a well developed egg was found inside. Had this pair followed their natural course this would have been the first recorded reproduction ever of this bird within the whole of the Spanish territory.

Peregrine (*Falco peregrinus*). N.P. + Mall + C.: Falcó, falcó pelegrí; A.M.: Falcó munterí; Cast.: Halcón común o peregrino (35).

This species is a common resident, with a density of 30/40 breeding pairs. Moll (1957), differentiated the Peregrine from the indigenous subspecies "*brookey*", but this hasn't been investigated any further.

As opposed to the European population, the Minorcan Peregrines seemingly haven't suffered the abuse of chemical products

35. Peregrine *(Falco peregrinus)*

such as D.D.T, which has caused numbers to drop dramatically over past decades.

But it has suffered due to chick or nest pillaging, and more than one Peregrine dies each year in the hands of ignorant and unscrupulous hunters.

Some pairs have disappeared from coastal locations due to excessive tourism. And finally, one has to obviously expect abandoned nests due to repetitive disturbances from land or sea during breeding periods.

The presence of Peregrins is more common inland and on sea cliffs, where there is an abundance of prey. But it can also be observed in woodlands, open fields, even in towns and villages looking to capture pigeons. In December and January the breeding season starts and pairs can be seen spinning and calling. The lay takes place in February/March, normally 3 eggs. Incubation lasts 28-29 days. After 30/40 days the first attempts to fly around the nest commence. After June the young chick emancipates itself. In Minorca we have studied the average success rate of chicks that manage to survive their first flight. The result was of almost 2 chicks per pair/year. Naturally, many die during the first year of their life.

Falcons capture their prey in mid air, aided by their eyesight and agility: they can reach 400Km/ph in dizzy flying dives. Their prey varies from warblers to ducks, pigeons or aquatic birds, depending on the area.

ORDER GALLIFORMES

FAMILY PHASIANIDAE

Red-legged Partridge (*Alectoris rufa*). N.P.: Perdiu; A.M.: Perdiu cama-roja, cama vermella, tita; Mall + C.: Perdiu roja; Cast.: Perdiz común **(36)**.

An abundant and well-known species much in demand among hunters. Due to its periodical repopulation in hunting areas and private estates numbers are kept up to compensate the hunting losses.

It is difficult to define the Partridge's habitat, but it can be found in open grounds, cultivated land, scrubs, near woodlands and even in forests. They are normally in small flocks or family groups. They run rather than fly, and only do so in dangerous situations,

36. Red-legged Partridge *(Alectoris rufa)*

and never too far or for too long.

During springtime and after mating, they build their nests on ground, concealed amongst vegetation, and lay 10/16 eggs incubated during 23/26 days by the female; sometimes the male incubates too, only when there is more than one lay. This high reproduction rate is explained by the fact that this species has many natural predators (especially man). The chicks leave the egg the minute the eggshell breaks and follows the mother.

The Partridge's diet is based on seeds, sproutings and small invertebrates. Possibly the Partridge was introduced to Minorca a few centuries ago for hunting purposes. Two other members of the same family were introduced to the island at the beginning of the century, the barbary partridge and the francolin, but they both disappeared soon after.

It is important to mention that the introduction of foreign species not natural the region (both animals and plants) always creates an ecological unbalance, sometimes producing severe and uncontrollable damage, as well as endangering the genetic diversity of living creatures, which should be carefully controlled.

Quail (*Coturnix coturnix*). N.P.: Guàtlera; A.M.: Guàtlera forastera o moreneta; Mall.: Guàtlera; C.: Guatlla, Cast.: Codorniz (37).

A small bird much more known by hunters than by ornithologists.

This bird's habitat are grain fields, where they build a nest on ground level moving to bushy areas in winter.

It is a migrator that arrives in spring and leaves in fall. In Minorca we have a resident population all year round, and according to Moll this population has formed the subspecies *minoricensis*.

This bird is quite difficult to observe and its presence can be detected by its call.

37. Quail *(Coturnix coturnix)*

The Quail population has dropped during the last few years due to various factors: on one hand neglected fields and hunting, and on the other hand the agricultural mechanization destroying nests at harvest time. We know that every now and then repopulation takes place with farm grown Quails, with the risk that this represents for wild specimens. Little is known about their eating habits, but it is expected to be similar to partridges.

In the Balearics 13 ringed quails have been recovered (12 from Italy and one from Germany).

ORDER GRUÏFORMES

FAMILY RALLIDAE

Water Rail (*Rallus aquaticus*). N.P.: Rascló; A.M.: Receló, gall d'aigua, gallet de riu; Mall.: Polla d'aigua, rascló; C.: Rascló; Cast.: Rascón **(38)**.

38. Water Rail *(Rallus aquaticus)*

Common resident all over Minorca especially in wet marshy grounds and streams. There is probably a resident population and a possible passage migrant population and some winter residents.

A secretive bird, it lives in thick reedbeds and other aquatic vegetation, where it builds its nest; it is rarely seen in the open, but is easily identified by its call. Es Prat de Son Bou and S'Albufera are common locations for this bird.

Its diet consists of a wide range of aquatic invertebrates, mollusks, insects and some vegetable matter.

Spotted Crake (*Porzana porzana*). N.P.: Rasclet pintat; A.M.: Polla groga; Mall.: Polla d'aigua; C.: Polla pintada; Cast.: Polluela pintoja.

The Spotted Crake has very similar habits to the water rail but is less abundant and known around the island. In fact there are only a few observations registered mostly in Es Prat de Son Bou and S'Albufera.

It is highly probable that it breeds on the island, but this fact has not yet been confirmed. Observations and sounds have been recorded all year round but we are not sure if they are common residents, a sedentary population, or just migratory and winter residents.

Little Crake (*Porzana parva*). N.P.: Rascletó; Mall.: Rasclet; C.: Rascletó; Cast.: Polluela bastarda.

Scarce visitor, with small number of observations registered. It is probably a scarce migrant and winter visitor that goes unnoticed.

Baillon's Crake (*Porzana pusilla*). N.P.: Rasclet gris; A.M.: Polla griseta; Mall.: Rasclet; C.: Rasclet, picardona; Cast.: Polluela chica.

No recent observations registered. Ponseti (1914) and Moll (1957) considered it a scarce resident, but this is questionable.

Corncrake (*Crex crex*). N.P.: Rei de guàtleres; A.M. + Mall.: Guàtlera maresa; Cat.: Guatlla maresa; Cast.: Guión de codornices.

There is little information at present about this species, the few observations registered tend to indicate that it is a scarce and irregular migrator to the island. According to the bibliography and conversations held with older hunters, we see that in the past it was relatively frequent in wet areas and nearby woodlands. The regression suffered by this species in their original areas during the last few decades clearly explains the rare visits of Corncrakes to the island.

Moorhen (*Gallinula chloropus*). N.P.: Polla d'aigua; A.M.: Fotja petita; Mall.: Gallineta d'aigua; Cat.: Polla d'aigua; Cast.: Polla de agua **(39)**.

Common resident in any fresh water areas of the island. It is unmistakable due to its shape and colour, and although it is secretive, it often comes out into the fields. It has been observed all around fresh water streams, ponds and even aban-doned swimming pools.

Seemingly most Moorhens on the island are sedentary, but without doubt a few winter visitors and migrants join the local population. Breeding starts in February. They build the nest in marshes,

39. Moorhen (*Gallinula chloropus*)

well hidden. Lay 2/6 eggs, which both parents incubate alternatively for 22/25 days.

In Minorca, chicks have been observed as early as March right up to the beginning of summer, since they breed twice and even three times a season.

Coot (*Fulica atra*). N.P. + Mall + C.: Fotja; A.M.: Fotja grossa; Cast.: Focha común **(40)**.

40. Coot *(Fulica atra)*

The coot is present in all Minorcan wetlands; around S'Albufera des Grau, during a favourable winter over 6.000 specimens have been censed. The local population is sedentary, although it hasn't been properly censed it could reach up to 300 pairs, spread mainly around S'Albufera, Son Bou, Son Saura Nord, Lluriac, Morella, Addaia etc...

From the end of summer to December the European winter residents start arriving (recoveries of ringed birds have been made from the following countries: 2 Germany, 1 France, 1 Czechoslovakia, 1 Switzerland).

The average population of winter visitors changes from one year to the next, depending on weather conditions and situation of local wet areas, but it seems to have stabilized at an approximate figure of 2,000 specimens. Towards the end of January they start heading back to their places of origin.

The local coots start reproducing early, from March the little chicks can be seen in company of parents. The nest, made of waterside vegetation, is hidden on land or floating over water. The normal lay is of 6/9 eggs which are incubated by both parents between 21 and 24 days. They eat mainly aquatic plants from the water surface or dive into water.

Purple Gallinule (*Porphyrio porphyrio*). N.P.: Gall faver; A.M.: Gall d'aigua, gall de riu, gallinot d'aigua, fotja de front vermell;

Mall.: Gall d'aigua, gall faver; C.: Gall fer, gall salvatge, polla blava; Cast.: Calamón común.

Unfortunately this beautiful bird has faded away from the island.

Earlier authors mentioned that in the early part of this century it became scarce, and probably disappeared for good towards 1950. It possibly was a very common bird around wetlands and reed beds. The reasons for it becoming extinct are unknown, but could have been excessive hunting plus the alteration of wetlands.

In Majorca, after becoming extinct, it was reintroduced in 1990 to the Natural Park of S'Albufera d'Alcúdia with specimens from Doñana, and it seems to have climatized successfully.

FAMILY GRUIDAE

Crane (*Grus grus*). N.P. + A.M.+ Mall + C.: Grua; Cast.: Grulla común.

Cranes are migratory birds and only stopover while on route to and from migratory destinations. Observations are registered every year (from September to April), the best months being November and February. Most observations correspond to small groups or solitary specimens, which fly high, and probably don't even stop on the island. On stopovers, they tend to perch around large open fields and only stay a few days. The largest observation was recorded in November 91, a flock of 58 specimens.

The specimens observed on Minorca originate in northern Europe.

FAMILY OTIDAE

Little Bustard (*Tetrax tetrax*). N.P.: Sisó; A.M.: Gallina brava; Mall + C.: Sisó; Cast.: Sisón.

A rare visitor without any recent observations around the Balearics. Some captures were made during the first part of the century that imply it used to be vagrant visitor. The lack of recent observations is probably due to the population decrease that it has suffered within its own distribution areas.

ORDER CHARADRIIFORMES

FAMILY HAEMATOPODIDAE

Oystercatcher (*Haematopus ostralegus*). N.P.: Garsa de mar; A.M.: Frarot marí; Mall + C.: Garsa de mar; Cast.: Ostrero

A species of cosmopolitan distribution that occasionally stops-over during migration periods, especially around coasts and wet areas. It is usually a solitary specimen.

Black-winged Stilt (*Himantopus himantopus*). N.P.: Cames de jonc; Mall.: Avisador; C.: Cames llargues; Cast.: Cigüeñuela **(41)** (Photo 13).

41. Black-winged Stilt
(*Himantopus himantopus*)

The status of this beautiful wader on the island is as summer visitor and breeder, but both in small numbers.

During migration it can be observed in any wet area, but during the summer the best watching spots are Salines d'Addaia, Prat de S'Albufera (where a few pairs breed on a regular basis). Recently it has been found breeding in Tirant and Salines de Fornells.

We believe that they deserve special and urgent protective measures since the local breeding popu-lation does not surpass 10/15 pairs.

It is a species of cosmopolitan distribution and a summer visitor from southern Europe (In Majorca there is a colony of about 200 pairs at Salobrar de Campos). It spends winters in north and central Africa (a Black-Winged Stilt ringed in Majorca was retrieved in Mali). In exceptional cases the odd specimen may spend winters here.

Their favorite foods are aquatic invertebrates, worms and such that they catch in quiet waters.

FAMILY RECURVIROSTRIDAE

Avocet *(Recurvirostra avosetta)*. N.P. + Mall + C.: Bec d'alena; A.M.: Bec tort; Cast.: Avoceta **(42)**.

A striking black and white bird, it is the emblem for the prestigious Royal Society for the Protection of Birds (R.S.P.B.).

Around Minorca it is a scarce and irregular visitor, and is seen mainly around S'Albufera and Addaia during migration. It is more common in Majorca, where in 1985 one pair bred in Salobrar de Campos.

42. Avocet *(Recurvirostra avosetta)*

FAMILY BURHINIDAE

Stone Curlew *(Burhinus oedicnemus)*. N.P.: Sibil·lí; A.M.: Sebel·lí, xiribil·lí, xebel·lí, xibil·lí; Mall.: Sebel·lí; C.: Torlit; Cast.: Alcaraván **(43)** (Photo 9).

The Stone Curlew is a common resident (with possible migratory and winter visitors). It is probably the only one of our waders that doesn't need to live in wetlands, in fact it usually resides in heaths, wooded outskirts, chalk lowlands, rocky islets with scarce vegetation

43. Stone Curlew *(Burhinus oedicnemus)*

and dunes. The best areas to observe Stone Curlew are Punta Nati, Cap de Cavalleria, Mola de Fornells, Favàritx etc., although it can be seen all over the island.

In spring females lay 2 eggs directly on the ground, without building any kind of nest, and both parents incubate them during 25-27 days. After the breeding period, and as of September, they gather in flocks till next breeding season.

They are busybodies at dusk and into the night producing their distinctive nocturnal curlew-like call when flying.

Their diet is based on invertebrates such as snails, worms and some small vertebrates such as geckoes, frogs, etc... A Stone Curlew originally ringed in France was retrieved in Ibiza.

FAMILY GLAREOLIDAE

Cream-coloured Courser (*Cursorius cursor*). N.P.: Corredor; A.M.: Galera; Mall + C.: Corredor; Cast.: Corredor.

Rare vagrant that comes to Europe from breeding locations in Asia and Africa. There is only one reference in Minorca of a specimen captured towards the end of last century which is embalmed at the Ateneu Museum. Nevertheless, like in many other vagrant species, sporadic appearances cannot be dismissed.

Collared Pratincole (*Glareola pratincola*). N.P.: Polleta de la mar; A.M.: Oronella de prat; Mall.: Guatlereta de mar; C.: Perdiu de mar; Cast.: Canastera.

A scarce migrator, always in small numbers. Most observations correspond to solitary specimens or small groups, during the month of May around Lluriac, S'Albufera and Salines.

This bird tends to spend summers in Mediterranean countries and goes to Central Africa for winters.

Little Ringed Plover (*Charadrius dubius*). N.P.: Passa-rius; Mall.: Tirulil.lo petit; C.: Corriol petit; Cast.: Chorlitejo chico.

Little plover is a migrator and summer visitor, that can be observed from March to October and only exceptionally in winter.

During the 70s, it was confirmed as a breeder around the beaches of Binimel·là, Favàritx, Es Grau, Salines d'Addaia and Fornells.

No further investigation has been carried out during the last few years, but it is suspected that it only breeds in Addaia, considering that during the last ten years disturbances have highly increased during the reproduction period.

A specimen ringed in England was recovered in Majorca.

Ringed Plover (*Charadrius hiaticula*). N.P.: Passa-rius gros; Mall.: Tiruril.lo gros; C.: Corriol gros; Cast.: Chorlitejo grande.

It is a passage migrant mainly from March to May and from July to October, and some years there have been observations of solitary specimens or small groups spending the winter.

Their favorite areas on the island are Salines d'Addaia, Fornells and S'Albufera.

During migration it can be found in wetlands and beaches. It breeds in the northern part of Europe (as far as Iceland), and over winters in and near Mediterranean countries. A bird ringed in Germany and another in Scotland have been recorded in Majorca. On the other hand two birds ringed in Majorca were recovered in France.

Kentish Plover (*Charadrius alexandrinus*). N.P.: Passa-rius camanegra; Mall.: Tiruril.lo camanegra; C.: Corriol camanegra; Cast.: Chorlitejo patinegro. **(44)** (Photo 12).

A few couples breed in Ses Salines d'Addaia and Fornells, therefore it can be observed around these areas throughout the year.

During migration periods they are more frequent and can be observed around many more locations. There isn't an accurate census on the local population but it is estimated to be 30 to 40 pairs.

The Kentish Plover, ringed plover and the little ringed plover mainly feed on small invertebrates around coastal, sandy and muddy areas leaving their footprints behind them.

44. Kentish Plover
(Charadrius alexandrinus)

Golden Plover (*Pluvialis apricaria*). N.P.: Xirlot; A.M.: Xirlot rovell; Mall.: Fuell; C.: Daurada grossa; Cast.: Chorlito dorado común.

It is a scarce winter visitor. Most observations correspond to solitary specimens or small groups, generally mixed in flocks with lapwings. During the winter of 1980 a very large flock was observed in Minorca.

Their favorite spots are wet fields near wetlands (Tirant-Lluriac and the outskirts of S'Albufera).

This bird breeds in Iceland, Great Britain, Northern Europe and Asia, and migrates to Mediterranean countries during winter. A specimen ringed in Holland was recovered in Majorca.

Grey Plover (*Pluvialis squatarola*). N.P.: Xirlot gris; Mall.: Fuell gris; C.: Pigre gris; Cast.: Chorlito gris **(45)**.

It is a scarce irregular migrator and winter visitor. Observations of solitary specimens have been taken from August to May. It has been observed around Salines d'Addaia and Fornells, but also along beaches where they feed mainly on worms, mollusks, insects and also some vegetable matter. This bird originates in northern Asia's arctic latitudes.

45. Grey Plover (*Pluvialis squatarola*)

Lapwing (*Vanellus vanellus*). N.P.: Jua; A.M. + Mall.: Juia; C.: Fredeluga; Cast.: Avefría **(46)**.

46. Lapwing (*Vanellus vanellus*)

A well-known winter visitor, especially to the farming population. It arrives in October and observations take place till March. Rarely spotted in summer.

The Lapwing's commonest habitats in Minorca are wet fields around the aquatic areas of Son Bou, Es Prat, Lluriac, Salines etc. but it also visits inland farms.

During harsh winters it is more abundant, and observations of over 500 specimens have been recorded. It feeds on insects, snails, worms, spiders and some vegetable matter.

The origins of the Lapwing are mainly Central European. 3 ringed Lapwings have been recovered on the islands: one from England, 1 from Hungary and one from Germany.

Knot (*Calidris canutus*). N.P.: Gambussó gros; Mall.: Corriol; C.: Territ gros; Cas.: Correlimos gordo.

A scarce visitor. During the last 15 years only 4 observations have been noted (May and September). One in Son Bou, two at S'Albufera and one in Addaia. This bird breeds around the arctic regions, but during winter quite a few specimens reach South Africa.

Little Stint (*Calidris minuta*). N.P.: Gambussó menut; Mall.: Corriol menut; C.: Territ menut, terretitona; Cas.: Correlimos menudo **(47)**.

A small wader, an abundant passage migrant (March/June and August/September) and exceptionally present during winter. Its favorite locations on the island are: Salines d'Addaia and Fornells, S'Albufera and other wetlands and beaches.

It is normally found in small groups together with other species of waders, and it is a long distance migrator. It breeds in European and Asian arctic latitudes, and spends winters in Central and South Africa.

47. Little Stint (*Calidris minuta*)

2 ringed Stints (one from Finland and the other from Sweden) have been recovered on the islands.

On the other hand, a Stint ringed in Majorca was recorded in Ghana.

Temminck's Stint (*Calidris temminckii*). N.P.: Gambussó de Temminck; Mall.: Corriol de Temminck; C.: Territ de Temminck, terretita; Cast.: Correlimos de Temminck

A scarce and irregular passage migrant with very similar characteristics to the little stint. Observations taken during the last 10 years have been during the month of May and from August to October.

Purple Sandpiper (*Calidris maritima*). N.P.: Gambussó fosc; Mall.: Corriol fosc; C.: Territ fosc; Cast.: Correlimos oscuro.

An uncommon visitor. Only two observations registered, one in February 1985 and one in March 1986, of a solitary specimen at Son Bou beach. It breeds in the arctic regions and spends winters in Northern Europe, rare and few are the specimens that reach the Mediterranean.

Curlew Sandpiper (*Calidris ferruginea*). N.P.: Gambussó bec-llarg; Mall.: Corriol bec-llarg; C.: Territ bec-llarg; Cast.: Correlimos zarapitín.

A passage migrant, it breeds in the arctic regions. Observations start in April and go through September, May being the most favourable month to watch them.

The most frequented areas are Salines and S'Albufera. They are always in groups, sometimes mixed with other species. During their short stay on the island they keep very active feeding.

A specimen ringed during the spring passage (in Majorca) was recovered during fall in Bulgaria.

Dunlin (*Calidris alpina*). N.P.: Gambussó variant; A.M.: Gambussó fosc; Mall.: Corriol variant; C.: Territ variant; Cast.: Correlimos común. **(48)**

Regular but scarce passage migrant especially from March to May and from August to October. During the rest of the year it is more irregular. The typical areas are Salines and S'Albufera, but it has been observed around other wet areas and beaches and sporadically around more uncommon habitats such as farmlands, coastal rocky areas etc..

The birds breeding in northern Europe spend winters on the  Mediterranean coasts of Africa and subtropical African areas. A Dunlin originally ringed in Germany was recovered on the islands. Generally all limicolas such as the Dunlin feed on: insects, worms, mollusks, crustaceans etc... that they find in sand or mud.

48. Dunlin (*Calidris alpina*)

Sanderling (*Calidris alba*). N.P.: Gambussó tres-dits; Mall.: Corriol tres-dits; C.: Territ tres-dits; Cast.: Correlimos tridáctilo.

During the last 10 years it has only been observed on 6 occasions, always in May and around Son Bou and Salines de Fornells.

In Majorca, Ibiza and Formentera this is a regular passage migrant and winter resident. This information makes us wonder if it might go by unnoticed in Minorca, although we do have to take into account the favourable habitats for waders such as the Salobrar de Campos in Majorca, Salines d'Eivissa and S'Estany Pudent in Formentera.

Broad-billed Sandpiper (*Limicola falcinellus*). N.P.: Gambussó becadell; C.: Territ becadell; Cast.: Correlimos falcinelo.

There is only one uncertain observation registered in May 1983 at Addaia. It is a summer visitor to the Scandinavian peninsula, its migration route has a south east tendency. Rare and few are the specimens that reach the western Mediterranean.

Ruff (*Philomachus pugnax*). N.P.+ Mall. + C.: Batallaire; Cast.: Combatiente.

A common migrator, but not abundant on the island. The favourable watching periods are March to May and July to September, around Salines, S'Albufera, Lluriac etc... Normally they travel in compact groups of over 50 specimens.

During summer the male is unmistakable with its showy ruff of a wide variety of colours displayed for its nuptial ceremonies and fights, but this is only observed around their breeding areas (North Asia, Central-Western Europe). Unfortunately this is rarely seen on the island, with its late spring migrant specimens.

Jack Snipe (*Lymnocryptes minimus*). N.P.: Becassineta; A.M.: Cegó; Mall.: Cegall menut; C.: Becadell sord; Cast.: Agachadiza chica.

Besides marshy grounds, they often visit wet or inundated terrains and streams etc.. With its camouflage feathering, it is much easier to see in flight than on land.

It is normal that when flushed it suddenly rises in towering zigzags with a harsh "screech", before perching again.

The Jack Snipe is considered a migrant and winter visitor in Minorca. It has mainly been observed at S'Albufera and Prat de Son Bou. It breeds in northern Europe.

A specimen ringed in Norway was recovered in Majorca.

Snipe (*Gallinago gallinago*). N.P.: Becassina; A.M.: Cega rotja, rotgeta, begasina; Mall.: Cegall; C.: Becadell; Cast.: Agachadiza común (49).

An abundant winter visitor and passage migrant, of very similar habits and habitats as the Jack Snipe.

They can be observed from August to May, and the winter residents from October to March.

The snipe is a widespread breeder: North-America, Iceland, Mid and West Africa, most of Europe and the top half of Asia.

49. Snipe *(Gallinago gallinago)*

They seem to be faithful to their winter quarters, since a ringed bird during winter 83/84 was observed in the same spot 3 winters later. A ringed bird from Switzerland was recovered in Majorca, whilst 2 ringed snipes in Majorca were recovered in France and Italy. Their diet is mainly worms, insects, snails and some seeds.

The Snipe and the Jack Snipe are two species highly appreciated by hunters.

Great Snipe (*Gallinago media*). N.P.: Becassina reial; A.M.: Cegall; Mall.: Cegall reial; C.: Becadell gros; Cast.: Agachadiza real.

A rare visitor only observed on 3 occasions, twice in S'Albufera and once in Addaia.

Woodcock (*Scolopax rusticola.*) N.P. + Mall.: Cega; C.: Becada; Cast.: Chocha perdiz, becada (50).

No doubt that the Woodcook is better known by hunters than by ornithologists.

Woodcock's activity takes place at night and just before sunrise. It is difficult to watch them, even when they are near enough.

They normally take flight prior to beeing spotted.

Here on the island, it is a winter resident, arriving towards the end of October and remaining till February/March.

The number of woodcocks varies a great deal from one year to the next, depending on the severity of European winter. While on the island their favorite habitats are wooden areas such as oaks and less often pine or olive trees, it can also be found in wet woodlands near ravines.

50. Woodcock *(Scolopax rusticola)*

It breeds all around Europe, except the south.

2 ringed specimens have been recovered on the island, 1 from Hungary and 1 from Russia. Food: worms, insects, mollusks, seeds and grass.

Bar-tailed Godwit *(Limosa lapponica)*. N.P.: Cegall coa-barrat; Mall.: Cegall de mosson coa-roja; C.: Tètol cuabarrat; Cast.: Aguja colipinta.

A scarce and irregular passage migrant, the few observations registered have always been in September (Ses Salines) of solitary specimens.

Black-tailed Godwit *(Limosa limosa)*. N.P.: Cegall coa-negra; Mall.: Cegall de mosson coa-negra; C.: Tètol cuanegra; Cast.: Aguja colinegra **(51)** (Photo 14).

A beautiful migrant wader. In Minorca most observations take place during February, March and April (spring migration) and September (autumn migration), being rare during the rest of year. They are often found in small compact groups of sometimes over 40 specimens. In Minorca the most visited areas are Salines, Albufera and Lluriac, being less frequent in other local wetlands.

51. Black-Tailed Godwit
(Limosa limosa)

Whimbrel (*Numenius phaeopus*). N.P.: Curlera cantaire; Mall.: Curlera; C.: Polit cantaire; Cast.: Zarapito trinador **(52)**.

A rare passage migrant. Observed along coastal areas, it is a solitary specimen or travels in very small groups. This bird mainly breeds in Iceland and Scandina-vian countries.

52. Whimbrel *(Numenius phaeopus)*

Slender Billed Curlew (*Numenius tenuirrostris*). N.P.: Curlera de bec fi; Mall.: Curlera de bec fi; C.: Polit bec-fi; Cast.: Zarapito fino.

In Minorca we only have records of two specimens observed in June '74, around Salines d'Addaia and one specimen embalmed in the Ateneum, which was possibly hunted towards the end of last century/beginning of this one. It is a generally scarce bird that breeds in a few Siberian locations and migrates in winter towards Northern Africa.

Curlew (*Numenius arquata*). N.P.: Curlera reial; A.M.: Curlera, sibil·lí de la mar o de prat; Mall.: Curlera reial; C.: Becut; Cast.: Zarapito real.

A large bird that rarely stops over in Minorca during its migration. The few registered observations have been in wetlands and open fields. In Majorca it is a common and regular winter visitor, especially in Salobrar de Campos. It breeds in most of northern and central Europe and visits Mediterranean countries during the winter.

Spotted Redshank (*Tringa erythropus*). N.P.: Cama-roja pintada; A.M.: Gambussa pintada, xivita fumada; Mall.: Cama-roja pintada; C.: Gamba roja pintada, Cast.: Archibebe oscuro.

A regular but scarce passage migrant. On a few occasions small groups have been seen during winter and summer. This species' favorite areas are S'Albufera and Salines. They breed in the arctic latitudes of northern Europe and Asia.

Redshank (*Tringa totanus*). N.P.: Cama-roja; A.M.: Gambussa roja, xivita cama-roja; Mall.: Cama-roja; C.: Gamba roja; Cast.: Archibebe común. **(53)**

A common migrator and like the aforementioned species, it has been observed irregularly during summer and winter. Their favorite areas are S'Albufera and Salines.

It breeds all over the old continent (and in Iceland too). It also breeds in some favourable spots of Majorca but seemingly has never bred in Minorca.

53. Redshank *(Tringa totanus)*

Normally observed alone or in very small groups, it feeds at the water shore. Food: insects, crustaceans, worms, little fish and some plants. A Redshank ringed in France was recovered in Majorca.

Greenshank (*Tringa nebularia*). N.P.: Cama-verda; A.M.: Gambussa verda, xivita beig; Mall.: Cama-verda; C.: Gamba verda, Cast.: Archibebe claro.

A regular but scarce passage migrant. Most observations correspond to solitary specimens. During summer and winter they can be considered exceptional visitors. The areas with larger number of records are S'Albufera and Salines, but they have also been observed near other coastal and wet areas.

Marsh Sandpiper (*Tringa stagnatilis*). N.P.: Cama-verda menuda; A.M.: Gambussa siseta, xivita de bec fi; Mall.: Cama-verda menuda; C.: Siseta, Cast.: Archibebe fino.

A rare and scarce passage migrant, mainly observed from March till June and exceptionally during fall.

It is normally observed in solitary. The areas with the largest numbers of observations are Salines d'Addaia, Fornells and S'Albufera.

This species is of eastern distribution but not very abundant; therefore it is not surprising that it is scarce on the island.

Green Sandpiper (*Tringa ochropus*). N.P.: Xivita; A.M.: Xivita grossa; Mall.: Becassineta; C.: Xivita; Cast.: Andarríos grande.

A regular but scarce passage migrant from February to May and from July to October. Exceptional observations have taken place outside these dates, and most observations of small groups have taken place around S'Albufera and Salines. A bird ringed in Sweden was retrieved in Majorca.

Wood Sandpiper (*Tringa glareola*). N.P.: Valona; A.M.: Xivita borda; Mall.: Valona; C.: Valona; Cast.: Andarríos bastardo (**54**).

A scarce but regular passage migrant during April and May and again during September and October. It is more unusual during the summer, and so far it has never been observed during win-ter, but some speci-mens are probably present towards the end of March and beginning of October, like in the rest of the Balearics.

Their favorite spots are Salines, S'Albufera, Lluriac and Morella. They are normally obser-ved in mixed flocks with other waders.

In Majorca, so far, two specimens originally ringed in Germany and Sweden have been recovered.

54. Wood Sandpiper *(Tringa glareola)*

Common Sandpiper *(Actitis hypoleucos)*. N.P.: Xivitona; A.M.: Gallet de riu o river, xivita menuda, polleta d'aigua, poll o titeta de riu; Mall.+ Ca.: Xivitona; Cast.: Andarríos chico. **(55)**.

Small wader, can be observed all year round, but it doesn't breed here (or at least there is no proof).

Solitary specimens can be seen around swift streams and wetlands. The most favourable areas on the island are: Salines d'Addaia, Fornells and S'Albufera, during migratory periods it can be observed all around. An excellent area to watch these birds is along the stream of Sant Joan behind the port of Maó.

They are very common all over Europe; a ringed specimen from Sweden and another from Switzerland were recovered in the Balearics.

55. Common Sandpiper *(Actitis hypoleucos)*

Turnstone (*Arenaria interpres*). N.P.: Picaplatges; A.M.: Passarius marí; Mall.: Picaplatges; C.: Remena-rocs; Cast.: Vuelvepiedras.

A rare migrant with very few recent observations and most of them in September with the exception of one in December and another one in January. Always a solitary specimen.

In Majorca and Ibiza it is more regular, which makes us think that perhaps it goes by unnoticed here. So far it has only been observed in Salines d'Addaia and Fornells. This species is of arctic distribution and migrates long distances.

FAMILY STERCORARIIDAE

Great Skua (*Stercorarius skua*). N.P.: Paràsit gros; Mall. + C.: Paràsit gros; Cast.: Págalo grande (**56**).

It is a sea bird, rare during winter. The few observations registered so far on Minorca correspond to solitary specimens seen offshore.

The European population breeds on the coast of Scotland and Iceland. Their feeding habits include piracy in which they harry other seabirds, forcing them to drop the food they have captured for themselves. A bird ringed in Scotland was recovered here.

56. Great Skua *(Stercorarius skua)*

Arctic Skua (*Stercorarius parasiticus*) N.P.: Paràsit coapunxegut; Mall.: Paràsit; C.: Paràsit cua-punxegut; Cast.: Págalo parásito.

A seabird of northern distribution, it is rarely seen around the Mediterranean during migration or winter. Here on the island we only have one reference from H. Mester (a German ornithologist) who registered this observation in March 1982.

The other two types of skuas (pomarine and long-tailed) haven't been observed in Minorcan waters.

FAMILY LARIDAE

Yellow-legged Gull (*Larus cachinnans*). N.P.: Gavina cama groga; A.M.: Gavina gavinot, gallineta de la mar, gallinot, titeta de mar, de tramuntana, de migjorn; Mall.: Gavina; C.: Gavià argentat; Cast.: Gaviota argentea o patiamarilla **(57)** (Photos 15-16).

No doubt that this is one of the most common and known birds by all. Poets, writers, singers have all written about this bird

It also represents the symbol of freedom, and its constant use and abuse has certainly taken away its charm. This gull has changed its life style during the last few decades.

In the past this bird's habitat was basically the sea, but recently it is more frequent inland. This is due to their opportunistic habits, which has brought this bird to feed on man-produced garbage.

At present gulls eat everything: organic leftovers from dumps, carcasses, live animals they have learnt to hunt, chickens, diseased rabbits, young birds, reptiles, marine invertebrates and fish. In fact they are interfering negatively in many ecosystems and moving into ecological niches, not apt for this species. It has even caused aeroplane incidents by getting into the plane's turbines during landing or

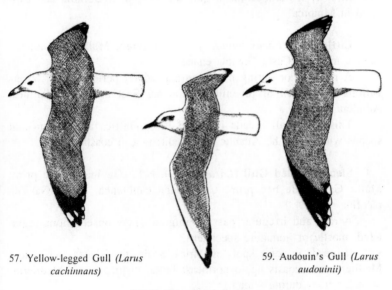

57. Yellow-legged Gull (*Larus cachinnans*)

59. Audouin's Gull (*Larus audouinii*)

58. Black-headed Gull (*Larus ridibundus*)

take off exercises. During the 80s serious measures had to be taken
in order to slow down the fast increase of gull population. On the
small island of Colom over 1.000 pairs breed.

The reproduction period begins in March. The gulls get together in colonies on sea cliffs or rocky islets. After building or re-
building the nest, they lay 2 or 3 eggs mainly incubated by the female during 25-33 days. Most youngsters leave the island, only to
return 2/3 years later when they are mature enough to breed.

Great Black-backed Gull (*Larus marinus*). N.P.: Gavina
grossa; A.M.: Gavinot; Mall.: Gavinot; C.: Gavinot; Cast.: Gavión.

Only one observation registered in 1982, by H. Mester (German
Ornithologist). Nevertheless this species has a northern distribution
and is considered a rare winter visitor in the western Mediterranean.

Mediterranean Gull (*Larus melanocephalus*). N.P.: Gavina
capnegra; Mall. + C: Gavina capnegra; Cast.: Gaviota cabecinegra.

A regular winter visitor on the Mediterranean coasts of mainland Spain, but only observed on rare occasions on the island, but as
many other birds, it might pass unnoticed amidst other gulls.

In 1967 a Mediterranean gull was ringed in Ucrania and captured in Minorca.

Little Gull (*Larus minutus*). N.P.: Gavinó; Mall.: Gavinó; C.:
Gavina menuda; Cast.: Gaviota enana.

A rare visitor during migration and winter periods. Most observations have been of juvenile specimens. Best areas are: Salines,
Albufera, Ports.

This little gull breeds in the Baltic countries and Russia and
spends winters on the Atlantic and Mediterranean coasts.

Slender-billed Gull (*Larus genei*). N.P.: Gavina de bec prim;
Mall.: Gavina de bec prim; C.: Gavina capblanca; Cast.: Gaviota
picofina.

A rare and irregular passage migrant. Few observations registered, mostly of immature specimens.

It breeds in some spots of Africa, Spain, the islands and eastern
Mediterranean coasts up to northeast India, visiting some Mediterranean locations during winter.

Common Gull (*Larus canus*). N.P.: Gavina cendrosa; Mall.: + Cat.: Gavina cendrosa; Cast.: Gaviota cana.

A rare vagrant on the island, solitary specimens have been observed. They breed in the northern part of Europe and on a smaller scale on the western coast of the Mediterranean.

As probably happens with other gulls, it is highly possible that some specimens visit Minorca on a regular basis but go by unnoticed amongst other gulls.

In January 1951, a common gull ringed in Poland was recovered here on the island.

Lesser Black-backed Gull (*Larus fuscus*). N.P.+ Mall.: Gavina fosca; C.: Gavià fosc; Cast.: Gaviota sombría.

An irregular passage migrant and winter visitor; solitary specimens with no more than 12 observations registered.

They breed on the coast of countries in north and central Europe. Only a few specimens travel to the Mediterranean during winter. A ringed gull from Denmark was retrieved in Ibiza.

Kittiwake (*Rissa tridactyla*). N.P.+ Mall + C.: Gavineta tres dits; Cast.: Gaviota tridáctila.

There aren't any registered observations of this bird on the island, but it has been occasionally observed in other areas of the Balearics. Due to the fact that it is a seabird, its visits possibly go by unnoticed.

Black-headed Gull (*Larus ridibundus*). N.P.: Gavina d'hivern; A.M.: gavina comuna, gavina petita, gallineta de la mar, baldritxa; Mall.: Gavina d'hivern; C.: Gavina vulgar; Cast.: Gaviota reidora **(58)** (Photo 17).

This little gull is common all over Europe but in Minorca it is only a winter visitor.

It is going through a phase of expansion and is colonizing Mediterranean territories. This fact explains the presence of non-reproducing specimens during the summer. It is abundant in built up coastal areas and even contaminated zones, but it also visits wetlands such as: ports (Maó, Fornells, Ciutadella), Salines d'Addaia, Fornells, S'Albufera, Lluriac, etc.

They visit farmlands, especially when recently farmed, where it is easier to find worms and other creatures left in the open by tractors.

26 ringed Black-headed gulls have been recuperated so far on the Balearics: 1 from Belgium, 3 from Poland, 4 from Germany, 3 from Finland, 5 from Russia, 1 from France, 6 from Czechoslovakia, 1 from Switzerland, 2 from Sweden.

Audouin's Gull (*Larus audouinii*). N.P.: Gavina corsa; A.M.: Gavina sarda, gavina de bec vermell, gavina de la mar, baldritxa; Mall.: Gavina corsa, Gavina roja; C.: Gavina corsa; Cast.: Gaviota de Audouin **(59)** (Photo 18).

Not long ago it was thought that this gull was in danger of extinction. After a decade of intense study it has been proved that it is going through an expansion phase. It has likewise been proved that it is very vulnerable to specific ecological disorders, for this reason it is protected by the law at present.

It is abundant on the other Balearic Islands in very large colonies. In Minorca, the breeding population has no more than 150 pairs, divided into two colonies. It is especially vulnerable during breeding season (April-June).

During spring and summer, they can be observed all over the Minorcan coast-line especially on the Northern coast. On the other hand, during winter it is very rare, which implies that there must be a dispersion movement which is under study at present.

During the last few years, it has been observed how some specimens of Audouin's Gull together with the Yellow-legged gull look for food around inland areas.

So far it hasn't yet reached the opportunism levels of the other gull and its diet is still based on fish.

The natural competition between the yellow-legged gull and the Audouin's Gull has often been observed in favour of the first. We suspect that the regulating population campaign of the herring gull will have benefits on the Audouin Gull.

FAMILY STURNIDAE

Gull-billed Tern (*Gelochelidon nilotica*). N.P.: Llambritja bec-negra; A.M.: Arvinjola bec-negra; Mall.: Llambritja bec-negra; C.: Curroc; Cast.: Pagaza piconegra.

It is a scarce, regular migrant; a mainly solitary specimen observed during April-May and September. The most favourable areas are S'Albufera and Port Maó. It has a of cosmopolitan distribution, mainly around the south of Europe. 2 specimens were recovered, one ringed in Denmark and the other in Russia.

Sandwich Tern (*Sterna sandvicensis*). N.P.: Llambritja bec-llarga; A.M.: Arvinjola cama-negra; Mall.: Llambritja de bec llarg; C.: Xatrac bec-llarg; Cast.: Charrán patinegro.

This beautiful tern used to be considered an occasional visitor to the island, but during the last decade it has been confirmed as a regular winter visitor.

The best spot to watch it is the Port of Maó. It is a very active bird that hovers and plunges into the water after small fish.

A bird ringed in Russia was recuperated in Majorca.

Common Tern (*Sterna hirundo*). N.P.: Llambritja comuna; A.M.: Arvinjola capnegra; Mall.: Llambritja; C.: Xatrac comú; Cast.: Charrán común.

A common breeder all round Europe, this bird specializes in long distance migrations (over 15.000 km on a single flight). It is common around the Mediterranean during migration periods, but in Minorca it was only observed once, in 1984 (Port of Maó). It certainly goes by unnoticed since it is a regular passage migrator on the rest of the islands and an irregular winter visitor.

Little Tern (*Sterna albifrons*). N.P.: Llambritja menuda; A.M.: Arvinjola menuda; Mall.: Llambritja menuda; C.: Xatrac menut; Cast.: Charrancito.

The smallest tern in Europe, only 5 observations recorded so far on the island; four during spring migration and one during fall migration. But like many other birds, it possibly visits us more often than records show.

There are two other species of terns, the Roseate Tern and the Caspian Tern, that breed in Europe, and they probably visit the island occasionally but no records have been taken. They have both been observed in Majorca.

Whiskered Tern (*Chlidonias hybrida*). N.P.: Fumarell carablanc; A.M.: Arvinjola mongina; Mall.+ C.: Fumarell carablanc; Cast.: Fumarel cariblanco.

Scarce but regular passage migrant. So far it has only been observed during spring (April and May), mainly around S'Albufera, in small groups or solitary specimens.

Black Tern (*Chlidonias niger*). N.P.: Fumarell negre; Mall +
C.: Fumarell negre; A.M.: Ronella de mar negra, arvinjola; Cast.:
Fumarel común **(60)**.

Scarce regular migrator with both passages, April-May and August to October. The best observation spots are S'Albufera and Port of Maó. Very active solitary specimen or in small groups.

The Black-Tern, (like the rest of tern species observed around Minorca) captures small aquatic invertebrates and little fresh or salt water fish. They breed in central Europe and migrate to Tropical Africa for the winter.

60. Black Tern *(Chlidonias niger)*

White-winged Black Tern (*Chlidonias leucoptera*). N.P.:
Fumarell alablanc; A.M.: Arvinjola d'ales blanques; Mall.: Fumarell
alablanc; C.: Fumarell alablanc; Cast.: Fumarel aliblanco.

East European distribution, rare visitor. Solitary specimens or
single pairs have been observed around ports and S'Albufera, not on
more than 10 occasions and always in spring, with the exception of
one observation in September.

FAMILY ALCIDAE

Guillemot (*Uria aalge*). N.P.: Pingdai bec-fi; A.M.: Pingdai de
bec prim; Mall.: Pingdai de bec fi; C.: Somorgollaire; Cast.: Arao
común.

Sea birds, they breed around the western Atlantic coasts and
Iceland, exceptionally observed around the Mediterranean coasts in
winter.

In Minorca there is reference of a captured Guillemot towards
the end of last century.

Razorbill (*Alca torda*). N.P.: Pingdai; Mall.: Pingdai; C.: Gavot; Cast.: Alca común (Photo 20).

A rare winter visitor observed on few occasions in Minorca. The last observation recorded dates back to January 85 in the Port of Maó.

This sea bird has a very similar distribution area to the guillemot, but in winter is more frequent on the eastern coast of mainland Spain.

It is known that 70% of the world's population breeds in the U.K. Two specimens ringed on the British Isles were recovered in Majorca.

Puffin (*Fratercula arctica*). N.P.: Cadafet; A.M.: Nas de foc, soldat; Mall.: Cadafet; C.:Fraret; Cast.: Frailecillo común.

A rare occasional winter visitor, although some fishermen from Ciutadella insist on having seen small groups during some winters at "Sa Barra"(fishing spot between Minorca and Majorca). 2 ringed Puffins from the U.K. are recorded in the G.O.B. files.

ORDER COLUMBIFORMES

FAMILY COLUMBIDAE

Rock Dove (*Columba livia*). N.P.: Colom salvatge o de roca; Mall.: Colom salvatge; C.: Colom roquer; Cast.: Paloma bravía.

Most townspeople know what a dove is. These town doves are descendants of the Rock Dove. The Rock Dove lives all over the island on rocky cliffs (inland) or along coasts. In fact wild doves build their nests on ledges in caves, holes, cliff sides etc. They breed in spring (twice or even three times a year) and lay 2 eggs which are incubated 18 days by both parents. Occasionally pairs have bred during winter.

Doves go to farmlands to eat seeds, and to often mix with domestic doves (they live freely on the island) and even breed together, the resulting hybrid[2] suffers from attacks by peregrine falcons, who live and breed in the same biotopes as these doves.

The Minorcan population seems sedentary. It's supposed the original distribution area of this species to be turkestan-mediterranean.

---

[2] They are not gifted, for instance, with the agility that natural selection has provided wild Rock Doves.

Stock Dove (*Columba oenas*). N.P.: Xixell; Mall.: Xixell; C.: xixella; Cast.: Paloma zurita.

Common in Europe, it visits Minorca irregularly during migratory routes and in winter. According to hunters some years very large flocks arrive and hang around open and essentially agricultural countryside. But there are few observations recorded by ornithologists.

Wood Pigeon (*Columba palumbus*). N.P.: Tudó; Mall.: Tudó; C.: Tudó; Cast.: Paloma torcaz (**61**).

A beautiful and large pigeon very common on the island. This species favours wooded areas (oaks and pine forests) and it is abundant in ravines too. They build their nest with flimsy twigs on tree tops. They lay 2 eggs and both parents incubate them during 17 days. It is normal for them to breed two or three times a season.

During fall and winter more observations are recorded, this factor indicates the increase of winter visitors and passage migrants.

61. Wood Pigeon *(Columba palumbus)*

Like other pigeons on the island this species visits open fields, where it feeds on seeds, fruits, herbs and even worms, insects and snails.

Turtle Dove (*Streptopelia turtur*). N.P.: Tórtera; A.M. + Mall. + C.: Tórtora; Cast: Tórtola común (**62**) (Photo 19).

The Turtle Dove is a common migrant and summer breeder on the island. The first visitors arrive around April and remain till October.

Its habitat is varied, oak and pine woodlands, shrubs, orchards, farmlands and gardens. They build plain nests on tree tops, and lay 2 eggs that both parents incubate during 14/15 days (usually twice a year). This species migrates to Tropical Africa during the winter.

62. Turtle Dove
(*Streptopelia turtur*)

ORDER CUCULIFORMES

FAMILY CUCULIDAE

Great Spotted Cuckoo (*Clamator glandarius*). N.P. + Mall.: Cucui reial; C.: Cucut reial; Cast.: Críalo.

An exceptional visitor, only 4 observations registered during spring, but it could be a regular visitor that goes by unnoticed.

Cuckoo (*Cuculus canorus*). N.P.: Cucui; Mall.: Cucui; C.: Cucut; Cast.: Cuco **(63)**.

63. Cuckoo *(Cuculus canorus)*

Migrators and summer breeders, they start arriving in March but it is during April when they are most abundant. The breeding population is scarce and lives in woodlands. It is easier to hear it than to see it.

Cuckoos have particularly unusual breeding habits. They are parasitic on other species of birds, laying their eggs in other species' nests and leaving them to raise their young. Female Cuckoos, have good control of the moment of egg laying: they often dash in and lay an egg while the host is away for only a few moments. The female Cuckoo ejects one of the host's eggs. The chick usually hatches ahead of the host's chicks, since it will eventually be much larger, as it needs all the food that the foster parents can bring in. It eliminates competition by getting under the host's eggs or newly hatched chicks and very slowly stretches up and tips them out of the nest. Cuckoos should not be misjudged by humans for this "cruelty", nature has produced this strategy as one of the ways of natural selection and evolution.

During August/September there is a large migratory passage. They feed on insects, especially caterpillars and worms, and spend winters in Tropical Africa.

ORDER STRIGIFORMES

FAMILY TYTONIDAE

Barn Owl (*Tyto alba*). N.P.: Òliba; A.M.: Òliba blanca. Òliba morena, miloca, maremiota; Mall + C.: Òliba; Cast.: Lechuza común. **(64)** (Photo 21).

A nocturnal bird of prey, it is widespread on the island.

They normally build their nests in barns, church towers, large tree-holes, old buildings, cliff holes and caves.

It is often but briefly seen at night in front of a car, (or simply with the help of a torch or moonlight)

64. Barn Owl *(Tyto alba)*

perched on top of an electric pole. They take off suddenly if molested.

Two factors can indicate their presence: one is their unmistakable call (drawn-out screech). The other factor are their excrements that they regurgitate in the shape of elongated balls containing remains of undigested prey. These excrements accumulate underneath nests and perching areas. From these balls their diet can be studied, consisting mainly of mice, rats, birds, reptiles and a few invertebrates.

In many parts of Spain the Barn Owl was persecuted on account of superstitions related to death. This brought about their indiscriminate hunt but fortunately these beliefs were of no incidence in Minorca.

The above mentioned and the lack of natural competitors has made it possible for an acceptable population level, but rat poison and road accidents are endangering this species. No studies have been made to cense the number of breeding pairs on the island.

FAMILY STRIGIDAE

Scops Owl (*Otus scops*). N.P.: Mussol; Mall.: Mussol; C: Xot; Cast: Autillo **(65)** (Photo 22).

More abundant around the island than the barn owl, and found all year-round in widespread habitats.

Its unmistakable call is heard at night in spring and summer (occasionally in winter).

Through its excrements we can say that its food is mainly based on insects and invertebrates (rarely mice, small birds or reptiles). Part of the Minorcan population are residents, and the other part are migrants and winter residents from Europe.

A ringed Scops Owl from Majorca was recuperated in Italy.

65. Scops Owl *(Otus scops)*

Although it hasn't been accurately censed we reckon there must be around 300 pairs. The major unnatural death factor are owls run over by cars.

They don't build nests but use nooks and crannies on rocky cliffs, tree-holes, buildings, and old bird's nests. They lay 4 to 5 eggs that are incubated by the female during 25 days.

Little Owl (*Athene noctua*). N.P.: Miula; A.M.: Mussola vera; Mall.: Miula; C.: Mussol; Cast.: Mochuelo común.

The information recorded so far indicates that Little Owls are regular passage migratory and winter visitors. Their favorite habitat are wild olive trees. There are few records of breeding pairs. But further studies have to be made in order to establish the status of this night bird of prey.

The recovery of an owl ringed in Germany is recorded in Majorca.

Long-eared Owl (*Asio otus*). N.P.: Mussol reial; A.M.: Òliba d'orelles; Ò. amb orelles, mussol gros; Mall.: Mussol reial; C.: Mussol banyut; Cast.: Buho chico.

This owl breeds on the rest of the Balearic Islands but it hasn't yet been proved that it breeds here, so further field work, and especially night auditions, are needed. So far we can only confirm its status as passage migrant and scarce winter resident.

Short-eared Owl (*Asio flammeus*). N.P.: Mussol emigrant; A.M.: Òliba d'aigua o de camp o d'albufera; Mall + C.: Mussol emigrant; Cast.: Lechuza campestre.

Rare passage migrant and winter visitor. And like the previous mentioned, further field work must be done in order to acquire more details.

A breeding pair was detected in Majorca at Salobrar de Campos in 1976.

ORDER CAPRIMULGIFORMES

FAMILY CAPRIMULGIDAE

Nightjar (*Caprimulgus europaeus*). N.P.: Enganapastors; A.M.: Boca ampla; Mall.: Enganapastors; Cat.: Enganyapastors; Cast.: Chotacabras gris (**66**).

While in flight this bird is easily mistaken for a cuckoo. The Nightjar's status on the island can be considered as a scarce passage mi-grant and summer visitor. Its favorite habitat are wooded areas (pine and oaks).

From March to July the distinc-tive male's songs

66. Nightjar *(Caprimulgus europaeus)*

can be heard around dusk and evening and since its mimetic feathering makes it difficult to observe, their song is a good clue to their presence.

They lay eggs directly on the ground, and incubate during 18 days. Normally they breed twice a season.

They eat nocturnal insects that they capture in flight with their mouth wide open. They like to perch on the roads which provokes a few deaths a year.

This migrator spends winters in Tropical Africa.

ORDER APODIFORMES

FAMILY APODIDAE

Swift *(Apus apus)*. N.P.: Vinjola; A.M.: Ginjola; Mall.: Falzia; C.: Falziot; Cast.: Vencejo común. **(67)**.

It is one of the most well-known birds since its habitat is mainly urban. Swifts are summer residents, they stay on the island from late March to October, being more abundant during migration periods. They are very abundant and can be observed all over the island. They build their nests on top of buildings, and also on cliffs, both inland and on the coast. It is normal for one swift to use the same nest year after year. They lay between 2/4 eggs which are in-

67. Swift *(Apus apus)*

cubated by both parents between 14/20 days. As they are aerial birds, they can feed, copulate and rest in flight. If, for whatever reason, they should fall to the ground, they would perish unless they happened to fall on an slope from where they could take flight. They feed on aerial insects and spend winters in Africa.

Pallid Swift (*Apus pallidus*). N.P.: Vinjola pàl·lida; A.M.: Ginjola clara; Mall.: Falzia pàl·lida; C.: Falziot pàl·lid; Cast.: Vencejo pálido.

Very similar to the swift, it is a summer visitor on the island, but more unknown. In fact observations on swifts should be classified as belonging to genus *Apus*, unless they are made under clear visibility conditions. They live on the coastal cliffs (mainly on the south coast) where, according to ornithologists F. de Pablo and S. Catchot they are more abundant than the swift. Both swifts normally mix. There are a few breeding groups in Maó and Mongofre Cliffs, this makes us think that they probably breed in other towns or inland cliffs. They spend winters in Africa.

Alpine Swift (*Apus melba*). N.P.: Vinjola reial; A.M.: Ginjola reina; Mall.: Falzia reial; C.: Ballester; Cast.: Vencejo real.

Regular passage migrant (March-May and September-October). Although it is not abundant it can be observed anywhere on the island. There is also a small breeding population located near Cala En Porter and El Toro, and possibly there are other little breeding groups. Further investigations are needed to establish the exact status/situation of this species on the island.

ORDER CORACIFORMES

FAMILY ALCEDINIDAE

Kingfisher (*Alcedo atthis*). N.P.: Arner; A.M.: Martinet blau, martinet; Mall:. Arner; C.: Blauet; Cast.: Martín pescador **(68)**.

This beautiful little exotic-looking bird is a scarce passage migrator and winter visitor. Sporadic observations have been made during summer, but this doesn't appear to be related to the breeding possibilities. The best watching spots are Es Prat de Son Bou, Es Prat and Sa Gola de S'Albufera and the Port of Maó.

During migration routes they can be observed in any wetland (they have even been observed near ponds; also on estuaries).

68. Kingfisher *(Alcedo atthis)*

With luck and patience they can be seen fishing. They skim over the water (salt or fresh) having launched themselves from their perches. They catch fish with their bill and swallow them whole head first.

A Kingfisher ringed in Germany was recovered in Majorca.

FAMILY MEROPIDAE

Bee-eater (*Merops apiaster*). N.P.: Abellerol; A.M.: Beierol; Mall. + C.: Abellerol; Cast.: Abejaruco común **(69)**.

A beautiful coloured summer breeder and passage migrant. Observations can take place as of April. They usually build nests in

69. Bee-eater *(Merops apiaster)*

sand-dunes, making burrows 2,5 meters long, with a roomy space at the end where 4 to 7 eggs are laid. Both parents take turns to incubate, which lasts 17/20 days.

The Minorcan population has decreased during the last few years due to the progressive degradation of the sand dunes.

Due to the excessive construction of the past 20 years, some of these habitats have disappeared, altered, or suffered the consequences of too many people and vehicles.

Only 12 years ago there was a colony of about 50 pairs around the Son Bou dunes, today there are none.

In Son Saura Nord ("Son Parc") a large colony almost ceased to exist.

Around the Tirant dunes, (not exploited at present) there is hope for recovery in the future.

The most stable colony is, at present, around La Vall dunes. Other small colonies or solitary couples are under precarious conditions in other areas of Minorca. It is most important to consider the protection of the larger colonies in order to avoid their continuous decrease.

In order to eat, they often fly in groups catching insects (bees, butterflies, dragonflies, beatles etc..) in mid-air, in the open countryside, never too far from breeding zones.

To rest they perch on electric poles, cables etc.

They have a very characteristic call on flight, and they migrate to South and Central Africa for the winter. 2 Bee-eaters ringed in France were recovered in Majorca.

FAMILY CORACIIDAE

Roller *(Coracias garrulus)*. N.P.: Gaig blau; A.M.: Xerraire, xerrador; Mall + C.: Gaig blau; Cast.: Carraca.

A scarce and irregular passage migrator, so far only 12 observations have been registered of solitary specimens or pairs.

Obviously there must be a few passage specimens each year that go unnoticed. In any case this is quite a tame bird found in open areas with scattered trees. They rest on top of trees or electric cables. They breed in most of Europe and northwestern Africa, spending winters in southern Africa.

FAMILY UPUPIDAE

Hoopoe (*Upupa epops*). N.P.: Puput; A.M.: Paput, Gall de Sant Pere; Mall. + C.: Puput; Cast.: Abubilla **(70)** (Photo 23).

Abundant and present all year round.

70. Hoopoe *(Upupa epops)*

They can be observed in many habitats, but tend to go for more or less populated, rural ecosystems and preferably with nearby vegetation: oak trees and pine trees. They enjoy visiting parks and gardens.

They feed mainly on insects and worms that they usually find while walking on the ground. They like fig trees, especially if there is a hole large enough to build a nest. They build nests in rural buildings. Their peculiar song is often heard around the Minorcan fields during spring time.

They lay 5/8 eggs that are incubated by the female during 15 to 19 days. The nest stinks due to a peculiar odour produced by leftover food and excrements, as well as secretions, produced by a gland that all birds have, which is extremely unpleasant in this particular species.

ORDER PICIFORMES

FAMILY PICIDAE

Wryneck (*Jynx torquilla*). N.P.: Formiguerol; A.M.: Formiguer, llenguerut; Mall.: Formiguer; C.: Colltort; Cast.: Torcecuello **(71)**.

This is the only representative of the picidae family found regularly on the island. There are a few winter residents. They are more abundant during fall migration and scarcer during spring migration. September is the best month to observe this bird. There have been insinuations regarding the possibility of it breeding, but it has never yet been proved, and in any case there aren't any summer observations.

Its diet is mainly based on insects, especially ants caught with its long sticky tongue (hence the Minorcan name). Another peculiarity is the way it turns its neck, especially when threatened by a predator, in imitation of a snake (with the head movement, hence the English and Spanish names).

71. Wryneck
(*Jynx torquilla*)

It is not easy to observe due to its mimetic plumage.

Its normal habitats are open woodlands, especially wild olive trees. Their call is very similar to the kestrel's. They breed all over Europe and go to Central Africa during the winter. Some specimens spend winters in Mediterranean countries.

ORDER PASSERIFORMES

FAMILY ALAUDIDAE

Short-toed Lark (*Calandrella brachydactyla*). N.P.: Torrola (petita); A.M.: Terrola, torròl.lera; Mall.: Terrolot; C.: Terrerola; Cast.: Terrera común **(72)**.

Abundant summer visitors and breeders, they start arriving towards the end of March and remain till the end of September or

72. Short-toed Lark
(Calandrella brachydactyla)

early October, being more abundant around the beginning and end of this period, due to the passage migrant population. These birds are found in the open, often treeless, countryside all over the island. They spend a lot of time on the ground, where they feed on insects and seeds.

They build their nests on the ground, protected by bushes, lay 3/5 eggs which are mainly incubated by the female during 12/13 days. It seems that they normally breed twice a season.

They migrate to North Africa for the winter. A lark ringed in Formentera during July '86 was recovered 2 years later in Morocco.

Lesser Short-toed Lark *(Calandrella rufescens)*. N.P.: Torrola de prat; Mall.: Terrolot de prat; C.: Terrerola rogenca; Cast.:Terrera marismeña.

Only one observation recorded on the island during March '75 at Salines d'Addaia. In Majorca it has also been noted on a couple of winter observations, and it could be an exceptional breeder. In any case, wet areas are the most favourable habitats for this species.

Thekla Lark *(Galerida theklae)*. N.P.: Torrola caraputxina; A.M.: Torrola o torròl.lera, caraputxada o caraputxina; C.: Cogullada fosca; Cast.: Cogujada montesina **(73)**.

Abundant local resident. They spend a lot of time on the ground, on open farmland and coastal stony areas. They can often be observed perching on Minorcan dry walls. They eat seeds and insects, depending on the season and build the nest on the ground: they lay 3/4 eggs which are incubated during 12 or 13 days. It seems like they breed 2 or 3 times a year.

73. Thekla Lark *(Galerida theklae)*

Skylark (*Alauda arvensis*). N.P.. Alosa; A.M.: Torrola o torròl.lera grossa, alova; Mall.: Terrola; C.: Alosa; Cast.: Alondra común.

A passage migrant and winter visitor, some years more abundant than others. The best months to observe this bird are from December to April, although they have been seen as isolated passage migrants from September to November and May.

This bird, typical of open fields, enjoys walking on the ground in groups and eating grains-seeds, insects and worms.

FAMILY HIRUNDINIDAE

Sand Martin (*Riparia riparia*). N.P.: Vinjolita o oronella de vorera; Mall: Cabot de vorera; C.: Oreneta de ribera; Cast.: Avión zapador.

A common visitor during passage migration (March to May and August to October). It is normal to observe them in large groups intermingled with swallows hunting for insects all over the island.

At dusk they tend to concentrate around wet areas, usually rich in prey such as mosquitoes, and they sleep on reed-beds.

It is an abundant summer visitor and breeder all around Europe and North Africa, spending winters in Tropical Africa. Some ringed specimens from Minorca have been later located in different European countries such as France, Switzerland, Denmark and England.

Crag Martin (*Ptyonoprogne rupestris*). N.P.: Vinjolita o oronella de penyal; Mall.: Cabot de roca; C.: Roquerol; Cast.: Avión roquero.

Scarce passage migrators and winter visitors, their favorite habitats are coastal cliffs and steep riverbanks. This species is a common resident in Majorca, where a ringed specimen from Gibraltar was recovered.

Swallow (*Hirundo rustica*). N.P.: Oronella; A.M.: Ronella; Mall:: Oronella; C.: Oreneta; Cast.: Golondrina común (**74**).

An abundant passage migrant, and summer visitor (breeder). Especially from mid-April to mid-May and from mid-September to mid-October. During these periods they concentrate at dusk around reed-beds to feed and sleep. Contrary to what most people think, the swallow doesn't live in towns and villages like swifts do. This is due to the fact that many people confuse swallows with swifts.

74. Swallow *(Hirundo rustica)*

They build their nests in rural ecosystems such as barns, stables, farmhouses, farm buildings etc...

They catch insects on flight (mainly mosquitoes), and normally perch on electric cables, trees or buildings.

Most of the specimens observed (approx. 90%) during fall migration are youngsters in their 1st year of life (and very often last), and first migration. They are easily identified from adults by the length of their tail.

Most European swallows migrate to Central and South Africa for the winter.

In the Balearics over 30 ringed specimens from Europe have been recovered mainly from France, Germany and England. And about 15 swallows ringed on the islands have been recovered in these European countries, even one ringed in Majorca was retrieved in South Africa, (over 8,000km away). The first swallows start arriving in Minorca towards the end of February and the last ones towards mid-November. Nevertheless "absent-minded" specimens have been observed in December and January too.

Red-rumped Swallow *(Hirundo daurica)*. N.P.: Oronella daurada; Mall.: Oronella coa-rogenca; C.: Oreneta cua-rogenca; Cast.: Golondrina dáurica.

Scarce passage migrant. Normally single specimens are observed intermingled in flocks with other swallow species.

House Martin *(Delichon urbica)*. N.P.: Vinjolita: A.M.: Culblanc; Mall.: Cabot; C.: Oreneta cuablanca; Cast.: Avión común. **(75)**.

Common passage migrants and summer residents, they arrive in Minorca towards the end of February and can be observed until the end of October. They breed mainly in villages and towns. They

75. House Martin *(Delichon urbica)* build an almost round nest made of mud and lined with feathers on old and new buildings, which when possible they use year after year. The nests are usually close to one another since this is a very colonial species. They lay 4/5 eggs that both parents incubate during 13/19 days (managing 2 and even 3 lays each season). Their main source of food are insects caught in flight. They migrate to south-Saharian Africa in winter.

FAMILY MOTACILLIDAE

Tawny Pipit *(Anthus campestris)*. N.P.: Titina o titeta d'estiu; A.M.: T. sorda, T. sorda sibil.lina; Mall.: Titina; C.: Trobat; Cast.: Bisbita campestre.

Migrant passage and common summer breeder, but not abundant, they begin to arrive towards the end of March and remain till about the end of September.

Their habitats include dunes, sandy heaths and open country with little vegetation. Most observations are of solitary specimens or pairs, usually uttering their characteristic call in high display flight.

Their diet is mainly based on insects and other invertebrates that they find while walking. They nest on the ground where they take advantage of small holes and lay 4/5 eggs which are incubated for 2 weeks. The European specimens spend winters in Tropical Africa.

Tree Pipit *(Anthus trivialis)*. N.P.: Titeta o titina d'arbre; A.M.: Titeta sorda, T. forastera; Mall.: Titina dels arbres; C.: Piula dels arbres; Cast.: Bisbita arbóreo.

A scarce passage migrant, mainly during April and September. Small groups or solitary specimens can be observed in coastal areas. They enjoy perching on trees or bushes more than other pipits. This species breeds all over Europe and spends winters in Tropical Africa.

Meadow Pipit *(Anthus pratensis)*. N.P.: Titeta o titina sorda; Mall.: Titina sorda; C.: Titella; Cast.: Bisbita común. **(76)**.

Common passage migrant and winter resident, abundant from October to March and scarce during September and April, exceptional in May. They spend much of their time running in open country in groups searching for worms, insects and seeds. They breed in Greenland, Iceland, and north and central Europe, migrating to Mediterranean countries for winter.

76. Meadow Pipit *(Anthus pratensis)*

In the Balearics we have records of 12 retrievals: 4 from Russia, 3 from Finland, 3 from Switzerland, 2 from Belgium.

Rock/Water Pipit *(Anthus spinoletta)*. N.P.: Titina o titeta de muntanya; A.M.: T. sorda de prat; Mall: Titina de muntaya; C.: Grasset; Cast.: Bisbita ribereño (alpino y costero).

Scarce passage migrant and winter visitor. Common from October to March and rare in April/May and September. These are a rather solitary species and prefer wet areas as habitats. The sub-species mostly identified on the island is the *spinoletta*.

Richard's Pipit *(Anthus novaeseelandiae)*. N.P.: Titeta o titina grossa; Mall.: Titina grossa; C.: Piula grossa; Cast.: Bisbita de Richard.

An exceptional pipit on the island, only one observation was made on the island, in autumn 1982. Breeds in eastern Asia, not rare as vagrant to Europe, especially in Autumn.

Red-throated Pipit *(Anthus cervinus)*. N.P.: titeta o titina gola-roja; A.M.: T. sorda; Mall.: Titina gola-roja; C.: Piula gola-roja Cast.: Bisbita gorgirrojo.

Few observations (under 10) have been made on the island, and only during springtime (April/May). This species had not been quoted before 1984. We believe it is a spring migrant and more common than it appears to be, since when it has winter feathering (especially females) it is more like other pipits. They are regularly observed in Majorca during spring.

Small groups (under 10 specimens) have been observed on the island. Their favourite spots are coasts and wet areas. They breed in northern Europe and Asia (in arctic latitudes).

Yellow/Blue-headed Wagtail (*Motacilla flava*). N.P.: Titina o titeta groga; Mall.: Xàtxero groc; C.: Cuereta groga; Cast.: Lavandera boyera.

Common passage migrants, which is rather surprising taking into account that they are summer breeders in the rest of the Balearics. This fact is probably due to unknown ecological reasons.

Nevertheless, large flocks can be observed from the end of February to the end of May, and back again from the end of August to mid-October. They mainly go for wet fields (preferably near cattle) and wet areas with insects and worms. Large groups get together at night to sleep on reed-beds such as Son Bou.

Two ringed pipits have been recovered; one from Italy and another from Germany. There are a large number of sub-species out of which the most frequent is *iberiae*. There have also been specimens identified as *flavissima, cinerocapilla, thunbergi* and *flava*, which indicates the multinational source of migrants. At least two Yellow/Blue-Headed Wagtails have been recovered in the Balearics, one from Italy and the other from Germany.

They are summer residents all over Europe and northeast Africa, and migrate to Tropical Africa in winter.

Grey Wagtail (*Motacilla cinerea*). N.P.: Titeta o titina torrentera; Mall:. Xàtxero cendrós; C.: Cuereta torrentera; Cast.: Lavandera cascadeña.

A scarce passage migrant and winter resident, its favorite habitat are wet areas (including small puddles), but they frequent cattle fields where they feed on insects attracted by cattle. It is a solitary specimen, and its only group activity is when it goes to sleep at night.

Pied/White Wagtail (*Motacilla alba*). N.P.: Titeta o titina blanca A.M.: T. Blava, t. maleita, t. de coa llarga; Mall.: T. de coa llarga; C.: Cuereta blanca; Cast.: Lavandera blanca (común y enlutada) **(77)** (Photo 30).

77. Pied/White Wagtail *(Motacilla alba)*

A common and abundant passage migrant and winter resident, from mid-October to mid-March, the Pied/White Wagtail is one of Minorca's most frequent birds.

They normally walk alone or in small spaced groups in open areas where they search for worms and other little creatures.

They often visit wet areas (natural or manmade) where large groups concentrate. They tend to walk along "public roads" too.

At dusk they get together in large flocks to go to sleep. They normally sleep in trees close to human settlements or in reed-beds such as at Son Bou. They originate in Central Europe. 11 ringed birds have been retrieved so far on the island: 8 from Switzerland, 2 from Germany, 1 from Czechoslovakia. On the other hand wagtail ringed in Majorca have been retrieved 2 in Czechoslovakia, 1 in France, 1 in Sweden.

The subspecies most frequently found on the island is *M. alba; M. alba yarrellii* has been found as well.

FAMILY TROGLODYTIDAE

Wren *(Troglodytes troglodytes)*. N.P.: Salvatget; Mall: Passaforadí; C.: Cargolet; Cast.: Chochín.

Moderate winter visitor. Earlier ornithologists (Ponsetí, Munn, Moll) considered Wrens year-round residents and breeders; this fact is not impossible, but certainly strange, since there havent been drastic changes on the island ecosystems causing the extinction of breeding pairs.

In Majorca and Ibiza this species is a common year-round resident. However a curious observation was made in June 1984 of a pair singing in Sant Joan, which makes us think of the possibility of occasional breeding. Today the only definite information we have is that it is a regular winter visitor, more or less abundant, depending on the year.

They are mainly observed in areas of low vegetation i.e.: Mola de Fornells, Cavalleria, Marina de Cala Mesquida, and Prat de

S'Albufera. This species has secretive habits; therefore it may be present in many other habitats. Their call is very distinctive and can be heard throughout the year. They are present all round Europe and only the northern population move south during winters.

FAMILY PRUNELLIDAE

Dunnock (*Prunella modularis*). N.P.: Xalambrí; A.M.: Pardal moro, pardal de bardissa; Mall: Xalambrí; C.: Pardal de bardissa; Cast.: Acentor común.

It is a discreetly abundant winter visitor with a selection of habitats: steep river banks, orchards and woods (less abundant); a rather secretive bird which tends to shuffle along the ground by itself or in very small groups.

The Dunnock eats mainly insects, worms, seeds and fruits; it normally arrives in Minorca towards the end of October and stays till mid-March. It arrives here from different European countries according to the proven ringed retrievals: 1 from Sweden, 6 from Switzerland, 2 from Germany and 1 from Italy.

Alpine Accentor (*Prunella collaris*). N.P.: Xalambrí de muntanya; A.M.: Xalambrí tacat; Mall.: Xalambrí de muntanya; C.: Cercavores; Cast.: Acentor alpino.

A scarce winter visitor, regular on the island from November to March. Its favorite habitats are rocky mountain slopes, here on Minorca it is found in El Toro and Santa Àgueda. It is a very tame species and at El Toro it walks on the tarmac. Its looks and behaviour are reminiscent of the house sparrow while its eating habits are very similar to the Dunnock's.

FAMILY TURDIDAE

Robin (*Erithacus rubecula*). N.P.: Ropit; Mall.: Ropit; C.: Pitroig; Cast.: Petirrojo. **(78)** (Photo 29).

In winter the Robin is the most characteristic and probably the most abundant species (in absolute terms) in the Minorcan countryside.

With their unmistakable aspect, they can be found everywhere with a minimum vegetation, even gardens, yards etc.. During autumn they feed on fruits from small trees or bushes, and when spring arrives and insects become abundant, they switch to them.

78. Robin *(Erithacus rubecula)*

During the last two weeks of October, the migratory passage of Robins on route to North Africa is abundant, at this time the winter residents start arriving. The fact that there isn't a sedentary population on the Balearics yet there is in other more unfavorable latitudes such as Andalusia, North Africa and even the Canary islands is surprising.

Over 270 (recuperated ringed Robins) have been recorded in the Balearics from outside Spain: 60 from Sweden, 54 from Switzerland, 37 from Germany, 30 from France, 28 from Finland, 22 from Poland, 12 from Denmark, 10 from Czechoslovakia, 9 from Russia, 4 from Italy, 3 from Norway, 3 from England, 1 from Austria, 1 from old Yugoslavia, 1 from Belgium, 1 from Holland. On the other hand, of over 4,000 Robins ringed in Minorca 13 have been located as follows: 8 in Algeria, 1 in Germany, 1 in Finland, 1 in Czechoslovakia, 1 in Girona and 1 in the Columbretes Islands.

Ringing has allowed us to observe that about 80% of Robins arriving in Minorca are young specimens (under 1 year of age).

In Minorca, like the rest of the Balearics, thousands of robins are illegally hunted each year, and many others die in the hands of wild cats and in road accidents.

Nightingale *(Luscinia megarhynchos)*. N.P.: Rossinyol; Mall. + C.: Rossinyol; Cast.: Ruiseñor común.

A common summer breeder which is very popular for its highly developed, pleasant song.

In fact, this bird's song is the most important factor to detect its presence, since it has very discreet and secretive habits.

They start to arrive in April intermingling with passage migrants of the same species and remain till October.

The males start singing as soon as they arrive in order to attract the females, and begin the breeding season.

They build their nest in woods, steep river banks, using dry leaves and lined with fine grasses on bushes or low trees. They lay 4/5 eggs incubated by females during 13/14 days.

They tend to be loyal to their breeding locations and usually live over 5 years.

They are a species of European distribution and breed in north Africa, central and southern Europe and Asia. They spend winter in Tropical Africa.

Bluethroat (*Luscinia svecica*). N.P.: Blaveta; Mall.: Blaveta; C.: Cotxa blava; Cast.: Pechiazul **(79)**.

79. Bluethroat *(Luscinia svecica)*

A regular but scarce passage migrant and winter visitor, this species has very discreet habits and the best areas with over 90% of observations are Prat de Son Bou, and S'Albufera. Other areas such as Prat of Son Saura Nord, Son Saura South and Cala En Porter might receive a more reduced number of specimens.

So far, only the subspecies *cyanecula* has been registered. They eat insects, worms and other invertebrates, as well as vegetal matter. They mainly breed in the Northern part of Europe, 2 recoveries have taken place: 1 from Holland in Majorca and one from Belgium in Minorca.

Black Redstart (*Phoenicurus ochruros*). N.P.: Coa-rotja de barraca; A.M.: Coa-rotja, coeta rotja, c. de barraca, c. fosca, ferreret; Mall.: Coa-roja de barraca, C.: Cotxa fumada, Cast.: Colirrojo tizón. **(80)**.

An abundant passage migrant and winter resident, it arrives at the beginning of October and remains till March, being a rare visitor around the end of September and April/May

Their habitat is mainly in open spaces, farmlands, rock fences and cliffs. They enjoy perching on dry walls, rural and town buildings.

Normally a solitary specimen, they only get together in flocks during migration.

80. Black Redstart *(Phoenicurus ochruros)*   81. Redstart *(Phoenicurus phoenicurus)*

Very often they spend nights on beams, cowsheds, garages etc. They mainly eat insects on flight or from the ground, worms and some vegetable matter.

They breed in most of central Europe. So far the following information on ringed birds has been recorded on the island: 21 from Germany, 6 from Switzerland, 3 from Belgium, 3 from France, 1 from Czechoslovakia.

Redstart *(Phoenicurus phoenicurus)*. N.P.: Coeta-rotja reial; A.M.: coa-rotja, coeta-rotja; Mall.: Coa-rotja; C.: Cotxa cua-roja; Cast.: Colirrojo real **(81)**.

Frequent during passage migrations (April/May and September/October). As a migrator it can be found in different habitats but tends to concentrate in coastal areas.

Their number can drastically change from one day to the next, mainly depending on meteorological conditions.

They tend to perch on trees and bushes much more than the black redstart. They breed in Europe and migrate to Africa for winter. The following registrations of ringed birds have been taken so far: 4 from Germany, 1 from Italy, 1 from Belgium, 1 from Russia, 1 from France, 1 from Swizerland, 1 from Sweden.

Whinchat *(Saxicola rubetra)*. N.P.: Vitrac foraster; A.M.: Vitrac bord; Mall.: Bitxac barba-roja; C.: Bitxac rogenc; Cast.: Tarabilla norteña **(82)**.

Passage migrants and exceptional winter visitors, they are especially frequent during April, May and September, where they can be found anywhere, but they tend to concentrate in coastal areas. It is a very tame species which makes observations much easier. In Majorca

82. Whinchat *(Saxicola rubetra)*   83. Stonechat *(Saxicola torquata)*

it has been found breeding on a couple of occasions, perhaps accidental ones.

They breed in most of Europe and spend winters in Tropical Africa. In Majorca there was a recovery of a Winchat ringed in Germany.

Stonechat *(Saxicola torquata)*. N.P.: Vitrac; Mall.: Bitxac; C.: Bitxac; Cast.: Tarabilla común **(83)** (Photo 26).

A common resident year-round, it is more abundant in the open countryside, especially heaths, moors, coastal areas and sand dunes. They normally perch on high spots, bushes, walls, stones, power cables etc., from where they can control the territory while emitting their characteristic call.

Their feeding is based on insects caught in flight or on ground: spiders, worms, seeds and fruits.

Most Stonechats observed on the island are sedentary, but there are also winter visitors and passage migrants. The retrieved ones have various origins: 3 are from England, 3 from Belgium, 1 from Germany, 1 from Switzerland, 1 from France. On the other hand a Stonechat ringed in Minorca was recovered in Algeria.

The reproduction period begins in March. They build their nest on the ground, protected by bushes; they lay 5/6 eggs which are incubated by the female during 14/15 days. Normally they breed 2 or even 3 times a season. There is proof that on the island they can live up to seven years.

Wheatear (*Oenanthe oenanthe*). N.P.: Culblanc (gris); A.M.: Fadrinet, viudeta, coablanca; Mall.: Coablanca; C.: Còlit gris; Cast.: Collalba gris **(84)**.

84. Wheatear *(Oenanthe oenanthe)*

A scarce passage migrant, especially from March till May and mid-August to mid-October.

Their favorite habitats are open coastal areas with sparse vegetation, they are very terrestrial birds and between flights they often perch on walls or stones. They breed in Ibiza, Formentera and isolated areas of Majorca, but not in Minorca. They breed all over Europe even in arctic latitudes and migrate to Tropical Africa in winter.

Two U.K. recoveries and 1 from France have taken place in the Balearics.

Their diet is very similar to the stonechats'.

Black-eared Wheatear (*Oenanthe hispanica*). N.P.: Culblanc roig; A.M.: Fadrinet roig; viudeta rotja, coablanca; Mall.: Coablanca rossa; C.: Còlit ros; Cast.: Collalba rubia.

A scarce spring passage migrator (March/May), it is mainly observed in coastal areas. They have a Mediterranean distribution and migrate to sub-Saharan Africa for the winter. So far during fall there has only been one registered in November.

Black Wheatear (*Oenanthe leucura*). N.P.: Culblanc negre; A.M.: Fadrinet negre, viudeta negra; Mall.: Mèrlera de coa blanca; C.: Còlit negre, merla de cua blanca; Cast.: Collalba negra.

This species has only been observed once (2 specimens in Favàritx, 1976) which makes us think this was exceptional. Although it is of Mediterranean distribution, it is a very sedentary bird that will only move short distances.

Rock Thrush (*Monticola saxatilis*). N.P.: Mèrlera vermella; A.M.: Coa-rotja; Mall.: Pàssera de pit vermell; C.: Merla roquera; Cast.: Roquero rojo.

Scarce migrants rarely observed on the island, but they could possibly be quite regular.

Observations have taken place in April and May, and from August to November, always in rocky areas of the Minorcan coastline.

They breed in mountain habitats, like Serra de Tramuntana in Majorca, and migrate to Tropical Africa for winter.

Blue Rock Thrush (*Monticola solitarius*). N.P.: Mèrlera (blava); A.M.: Mèrlera, tord roquer; Mall.: Pàssera; C.: Merla blava; Cast.: Roquero solitario **(85)**.

Common and present on the island all year round. Their typical habitats are rocky cliffs, both on the coast and inland, but during winter they also tend to go to open fields.

In their diet there is a wide selection of sometimes quite large invertebrates and vertebrates such as lizards or small snakes. They eat berries too.

On specific coastal spots and around steep river banks they present a high population density. They are always solitary, except during breeding season. They build their nests in rocky crevices sometimes in caves or old derelict buildings. They lay 4/5 eggs which are incubated by the female. Normally they only breed once a year.

85. Blue Rock Thrush (*Monticola solitarius*)

White's Thrush (*Zoothera dauma*). N.P.: Tord daurat; Mall.: Tord daurat; C.: Griva daurada; Cast.: Zorzal dorado.

A Siberian species that only reaches our latitude in exceptional circumstances. In Minorca there is only one reference of a White Thrush captured in January 1912 and it is embalmed and kept in the Ateneum.

86. Ring Ouzel *(Turdus torquatus)*   87. Blackbird *(Turdus merula)*

Ring Ouzel *(Turdus torquatus)*. N.P.: Tord de collaret; Mall.: Tord flassader; C.: Merla de pit blanc; Cast.: Mirlo capiblanco **(86)**.

Few observations registered, it is a rare passage migrant and winter visitor. All observations take place in coastal areas or rocky inland spots (Monte Toro, steep river banks etc.).

In Europe they generally breed in mountain areas and visit Mediterranean countries during winter, especially North Africa.

Blackbird *(Turdus merula)*. N.P.: Tord negre; A.M.: Tord morell, mèrlera negra; Mall.: Mèrlera; C.: Merla; Cast.: Mirlo común **(87)**.

A common resident with population increases during migratory and winter periods.

Blackbirds live in forest areas, preferably oak and pine woods. They live in orchards and steep river banks too.

In Europe this bird is common in parks and gardens. Their diet is varied, they enjoy worms which they find searching through the forest humus, and berries too.

A great number of these birds are hunted every year.

They breed between March and June. They build nests in cup shape made of little twigs, grass, dry leaves... located up trees, bushes etc... Normally they lay 4/5 eggs which are incubated by the mother between 11 to 17 days. They often breed twice a year.

This species breeds all round Europe and in winter we welcome specimens from mainly central Europe.

40 ringed Blackbirds have already been recovered: 15 from Switzerland, 10 from Germany, 5 from Italy, 3 from Czechoslovakia, 1 from Belgium, 1 from Hungary, 1 from Denmark, 3 from France and 1 from Poland.

Fieldfare (*Turdus pilaris*). N.P.: Tord burell; A.M.: T. burrell, t. reial, t. berberesc; Mall.: Tord burell; C.: Griva cerdana; Cast.: Zorza real.

An irregular winter visitor normally coinciding with very severe winters in Europe. The only observations taken are between November to March and often in small groups.

A Fieldfare ringed in Russia was recovered in Majorca.

Song Thrush (*Turdus philomelos*). N.P.: Tord (blanc); Mall.: Tord; C.: tord comú; Cast.: Zorzal común (**88**).

88. Song Thrush *(Turdus philomelos)*

Very abundant during passage migrations and winter, Song Thrushes are well-known to hunters and some are unfortunately caught using illegal methods. It has been worked out that in the 70s over 3 million Song Thrushes were captured every winter in the Balearics. This figure reflects massive murder more than a sport or hunting for home consumption.

The first Song Thrushes start arriving in September, but most get here in October and November and stay until March or April, when they become scarce.

They have a widespread habitat and during Autumn are more frequent near forest areas, where they sleep and feed on berries.

As winter progresses they venture off into open spaces, where they search for worms, snails and other little creatures that complete their diet.

Generally they are rather shy, and quite difficult to observe. In the Balearics over 340 ringed Song Thrushes have been recovered: 68 from Germany, 67 from Switzerland, 35 from France, 27 from Finland, 25 from Russia, 24 from Czechoslovakia, 23 from Italy, 15 from Belgium, 14 from Denmark, 10 from Sweden, 10 from Poland, 6 from Holland, 5 from Luxembourg, 2 from Austria, 2 from England, one from Hungary and one ringed in Jaen. Over 75% came from central Europe where they are legally protected.

On the other hand from the over 400 thrushes ringed in Minorca (by the G.O.B. team), the following have been recovered: 2 in Majorca, 1 in Valencia, 3 in Algeria, 3 in France, 1 in Luxemburg.

Over 50% of recoveries correspond to juveniles during their first year of life, since the majority die (or are hunted during their first 2 years of life).

If lucky some specimens can reach up to 10 years of age.

Redwing (*Turdus iliacus*). N.P.: Tord sardillo; A.M.: Tord petit, t. sard, t. sardo, t. cellard, t. calandrol, t. rotget; Mall.: Tord cellard; C.: Tord ala-roig; Cast.: Zorzal alirrojo **(89)**.

This bird is similar to the song thrush but smaller and less abundant during migration passages and winter.

The Redwing can be considered regular between October and March. But in fact it fluctuates from one year to the next. This is probably due to the northern distribution, so they normally move to mid-Europe for winters and are only abundant on the island during extremely cold winters.

89. Redwing (*Turdus iliacus*)

They have very similar habits to song thrushes, but tend to be more gregarious. In the Balearics over 14 ringed specimens have been recuperated: 3 from U.K., 3 from Italy, 2 from Belgium, 2 from Germany, 2 from Finland, 1 from Russia, 1 from Holland, 1 from Switzerland.

Mistle Thrush (*Turdus viscivorus*). N.P.: Tord rei; A.M.: Rei de tords, tord guia; Mall.: Grívia; C.: Griva; Cast.: Zorzal charlo.

Relatively common (although scarce) from November to February and unusual outside these dates. It is much larger than other thrushes.

They prefer forest areas combined with open spaces.

The best observation areas are La Vall and the surroundings of inland forest areas, they also frequent steep riverbanks.

Their call is very characteristic and easy to identify with a little practice. They are normally found in small groups. They breed all over Europe (except in northern Scandinavia) and in North Africa too.

In Majorca there was a recovery of a Mistle Thrush originally ringed in Germany.

FAMILY SYLVIDAE

Cetti's Warbler (*Cettia cetti*). N.P.: Rossinyol bord; A.M.: Xifles; Mall.+ C.: Rossinyol bord; Cast.: Ruiseñor bastardo.

Common residents all round the island, they live in wet areas, especially surrounding reed-beds, such as Prat de Son Bou, S'Albufera or steep river banks, as well as in humid woodlands, especially oak woods. They are territorial birds and breed in any wet area no matter how small. In Prat de S'Albufera we have calculated a density of 3 breeding pairs per hectare.

They have secretive habits which makes it quite difficult to observe them. Their presence is noted by their iloud song.

Breeding season begins in March, and they build a nest in a cup shape with small twigs, grass, fur, etc. They make it in a thick bush usually just above ground. They normally lay 4 eggs that the female incubates during 13 days. It seems that some pairs might breed twice a season. Their eating habits include small insects, other invertebrates and wild seeds.

Some lucky ones live up to 5 years, but the great majority don't reach two years. We have acquired this information through the recovery of ringed warblers during the last ten years.

Fan-tailed Warbler (*Cisticola juncidis*). N.P.: Butxac; A.M.: Butzac; Mall.: Butxaqueta; C.: Trist; Cast.: Buitrón **(90)** (Photo 24).

Common local residents, they live near damp areas, near streams and grain plantations. They are easily recognized by their jerky flight and characteristic call, especially in spring, and eat insects, spiders and seeds.

Breeding starts in March right up to July.

90. Fan-Tailed Warbler *(Cisticola juncidis)*

They build a small purse shaped nest, made of grass and dry leaves bound together with spider webs, and are located amongst low vegetation. They lay 4/5 eggs that are incubated by the female between 12/15 days, with 2 or even 3 broods each season.

Grasshopper Warbler (*Locustella naevia*). N.P.: Boscaler pintat gros; Mall + C.: Boscaler pintat gros; Cast.: Buscarla pintoja.

A regular passage migrant with observations in April and May, and from late August to late October. They have discreet habits.

Observations have so far taken place around Prat de S'Albufera and island of Aire. These areas are visited by ornithologists, but no doubt they can be seen around many other areas. It is curious that this species had not been recorded on the island until 1983.

Savi's Warbler (*Locustella luscinioides*). N.P.: Boscaler comú; Mall. + C.: Boscaler comú; Cast.: Buscarla unicolor.

This species had not been observed on the island till 1983, where various specimens were heard singing during May and June in Es Prat de Son Bou.

The following year at least 3 males were heard in Son Bou and one in S'Albufera.

The above mentioned makes us think that a few pairs could have been breeding during those years, but this fact unfortunately wasn't confirmed. However this bird has not since been observed, and further studies are required before clarifying their status on the island.

The Savi's Warbler is a summer breeder all round central and western Europe. They migrate to Tropical Africa in winter, which makes them passage migrants.

It is quite significant that none have been caught during the last ten years of intense ringing campaigns. It is important to note that it is a bird of secretive habits and easily mistaken with other warblers.

Moustached Warbler (*Acrocephalus melanopogon*). N.P.: Boscarla mostatxuda; Mall. + C.: Boscarla mostatxuda; Cast.: Carricerín real **(91)**.

This species had not been observed till 1982, since then a breeding nucleus has been detected in Es Prat de Son Bou and Son Saura North (about 30-40 pairs). It is possibly a recent colonizer coming from S'Albufera d'Alcúdia in Majorca where it is an abundant breeder. Some winters they have been ringed around S'Albufera

91. Moustached Warbler
(Acrocephalus melanopogon)

des Grau but they have never been detected there in summer. This fact could indicate winter dispersion of island residents or outside visitors.

They live well hidden in reed-beds, where they feed on insects and aquatic plants' seed. Therefore they are very difficult to observe, and it is only in spring when some males can be seen and heard singing on the highest points of the reed-beds.

They nest over water, mainly in reeds. Clutch-size and incubation periods are not yet clear.

Aquatic Warbler (*Acrocephalus paludicola*). N.P.: Boscarla d'aigua; Mall + C.: Boscarla d'aigua; Cast.: Carricerín cejudo.

A rare migrant on the island. With only 3 observations recorded, once in Es Prat de Son Bou and once in S'Albufera des Grau. It is highly probable that a few specimens go by unnoticed during migration periods, since they are of secretive habits and easily mistaken for others.

Sedge Warbler (*Acrocephalus schoenobaenus*). N.P.: Boscarla de joncs; Mall.: Boscarla; C.: Boscarla dels joncs; Cast.: Carricerín común.

A regular but scarce passage migrator (April/May and September). Most observations noted took place during scientific ringing campaigns. In fact, their discreet habits and their resemblance to other species causes difficulties and makes it almost impossible to determine direct observations.

The most favourable areas are Prat de Son Bou, S'Albufera des Grau, Prat de Son Saura North, but during migration they can appear anywhere.

They breed in most of Europe and migrate to Tropical Africa for winter. 2 specimens ringed in U.K. were observed in Majorca.

Reed Warbler (*Acrocephalus scirpaceus*). N.P.:Boscarla de canyís; A.M.: Rotget; Mall. + Cat.: Boscarla de canyar; Cast: Carricero común.

A scarce summer breeder and regular passage migrator, it is more abundant during fall than in spring. In fact we suspect that a few stay for winter but this is to be confirmed. Seemingly a few pairs breed in Son Bou and possibly in Son Saura North. Other wetlands with reed-beds may welcome occasional pairs. Further investigation is required in order to determine the true status of the breeding population.

The marsh warbler present in Europe is very similar in appearance, and it is very likely that it occasionally visits Minorca without yet having been detected.

This species breeds all over Europe and migrates to Tropical Africa in winter. A Reed Warbler ringed in Germany was seen in Minorca.

Great Reed Warbler (*Acrocephalus arundinaceus*). N.P.: Tord de prats; A.M.: Rossinyol de prat; Mall:. Rossinyol gros; C.: Balquer; Cast.: Carricero tordal **(92)**.

Although less abundant, its status in Minorca is very similar to the red warbler's, they can be found during migration periods and as summer breeders, always in small numbers. It is certain that they breed in Es Prat de Son Bou, possibly in Son Saura Nord and irregularly at S'Albu-fera although during migrations they can be found in a larger variety of habitats. They often emit their characteristic call from the top of reeds and bushes. Their distribution area is quite similar to the red warbler's, as well as their diet, based mainly on insects, spiders and other invertebrates.

92. Great Reed Warbler (*Acrocephalus arundinaceus*)

A specimen ringed during spring migration at S'Albufera d'Alcúdia was seen during the autumn migration in Son Bou.

Melodious Warbler (*Hippolais polyglotta*). N.P.: Bosqueta comuna; Mall.: + C.: Bosqueta comuna; Cast.: Zarcero común.

A scarce passage migrant, over 30 observations have been recorded (April to June and September to October) all over the island.

Birds of "hippolais" genres, they have secretive habits and are very difficult to identify, therefore most records are obtained through scientific ringing.

The Melodious Warblers' breeding areas are mainly located in southwestern Europe and northwest Africa, migrating to Tropical Africa in winter.

Olivaceous Warbler (*Hippolais pallida*). N.P.: Bosqueta pàl·lida; Mall. + C.: Bosqueta pàl.lida; Cast.: Zarcero pálido.

This warbler has never been observed with certainty on the island, yet taking into account that it is a summer breeder in North Africa and most of the eastern and southern coast of Spain and due to the five references we have in Majorca, we believe that possibly a few specimens stop over on migratory routes and pass unnoticed. In spite of this it must be very scarce, since it hasn't once been captured in 10 years of intense scientific ringing.

Icterine Warbler (*Hippolais icterina*). N.P.: Bosqueta icterina; Mall.+ C.: Bosqueta icterina; Cast.: Zarcero icterino.

Species with very similar status in Minorca to the melodious warbler. Like the melodious warbler all references correspond to ringed specimens (during spring migration campaigns on Aire Island), having only recorded 3 direct observations and 2 captures in other areas of Minorca.

To start with the spring passage seems more important in terms of numbers, however this is only due to its more ample study. Yet there are two important captures (one in July and another one in August) that theoretically correspond to birds in post nuptial dispersion.

The Icterine Warbler presents a summer breeding distribution in central and western Europe reaching eastern Asia. They migrate to Tropical Africa in winter.

Marmora's Warbler (*Sylvia sarda*). N.P.: Busqueret sard; A.M.: Busqueret coallarga; Mall.: Busqueret de coa llarga; C.: Tallareta sarda; Cast.: Curruca sarda.

The status of this warbler on the island is a little confused.

During the 70s the various observations by different ornithologists gave the impression that this species, though not abundant, was a common resident in Minorca. From the 80s onwards observations became increasingly scarce, and during the last few years there haven't been any. Consequently, we reckon that this species has became extinct on the island, probably due to the ecological displacement by another species of warbler, morphologically and biologically similar, the Dartford warbler, as suggested by some authors.

It is important to take note that being secretive and similar to the Dartford warbler, a few remaining pairs could go by unnoticed.

Their worldwide distribution area is reduced to western Mediterranean islands (they breed in Majorca and Ibiza), the eastern coast of Spain, and possibly some spots in North Africa, where some specimens hibernate.

Dartford Warbler (*Sylvia undata*). N.P.: Busqueret roig; A.M.: Busqueret pit-roig; Mall.: Busqueret roig coallarga; C.: Tallareta cuallarga; Cast.: Curruca rabilarga. **(93)**.

It appears that this species began to colonize Minorca towards the end of the 60s and 70s, moving Marmora's warbler from their usual habitats. The best areas to observe them are La Mola de Fornells and Maó, the area of La Vall and north of Ciutadella.

Dartfords are secretive and have hidden habits; they are more detectable by their song than by their presence and during the spring males can be observed singing in flight or on top of bushes.

Their main source of nourishment are insects and spiders. They usually build

93. Dartford Warbler *(Sylvia undata)*

their nest near the ground, often in thick bushy areas. They lay 3/5 eggs which are incubated by the female during 12/13 days, normally twice a year. Like the Marmora's warbler the Dartford warbler also has a Mediterranean distribution, but just slightly more extensive.

Spectacled Warbler (*Sylvia conspicillata*). N.P.: Busqueret trencamates; A.M.: Busqueret de bardissa; Mall.: Busqueret trencamates; C.: Tallarol trencamates; Cast.: Curruca tomillera.

Scarce breeders, their presence on the island was confirmed in 1981, when a few pairs were found breeding in Cap de Cavalleria. Since then it is scarce but regular at that spot.

During the last few years a few breeding couples have been observed around La Vall. Therefore it is possible that they breed in other areas.

This bird has a Mediterranean distribution, during summer they breed in the western area of the Mediterranean. They also breed on other Mediterranean islands such as Majorca and Ibiza, and migrate to North Africa in winter.

Subalpine Warbler (*Sylvia cantillans*). N.P.: Busqueret de garriga; Mall.: Busqueret de garriga; C.: Tallarol de garriga; Cast.: Curruca carrasqueña.

A common passage migrant, especially during April, May and September, with few observations in June and August. They normally concentrate in coastal areas of low vegetation.

There are some breeding references in Majorca and Cabrera, and it is possible that some isolated pairs breed here in Minorca, but this hasn't yet been confirmed.

This warbler is not as secretive as others, but due to its continuous movement it is not easy to observe.

They are of Mediterranean distribution spending summers here and winters in Western Africa.

Sardinian Warbler (*Sylvia melanocephala*). N.P.: Busqueret cap negre; A.M.: Busqueret, b. mascarat, nyecra, cap-negre; Mall.: Busqueret de cap negre; C.: Tallarol cap negre; Cast.: Curruca cabecinegra **(94)** (Photo 25).

It is one of the most abundant birds on Minorca (in absolute terms).

They are practically found in any spot with a minimum of vegetation: woods, shrubs, low under-growth, sand dunes, orchards, gardens, parks, roadsides etc...

The Sardinian Warbler is a very active little bird, it is always running about, searching for insects and other little creatures. During winter they also eat fruit.

They mainly breed between April and June, building a small nest in shape of the cup, preferably in bushes and in trees. They normally lay 4/5 eggs which are incubated 12/14 days by both parents, generally they breed twice a season.

On the island it is basically sedentary, even so, an occasional outside visitor might appear, accidentally so, since in the rest of its distribution areas it is also sedentary. Out of the 2.000

94. Sardinian Warbler *(Sylvia melanocephala)*

specimens ringed in Minorca, there hasn't been a single retrieval off the island.

On the other hand, a high number of Sardinian Warblers are killed every year on the Minorcan roads.

Orphean Warbler *(Sylvia hortensis)*. N.P.: Busqueret emmascarat; A.M.: Busqueret foraster; Mall.: Busqueret emmascarat; C.: Tallarol emmascarat; Cast.: Curruca mirlona.

This species has a Mediterranean distribution area. They migrate to Africa in winter, but must do so avoiding the sea crossing, since they are seldom observed on the islands.

In 1992, during a spring ringing campaign on Aire Island, 3 specimens were ringed. Therefore we reckon that each year a few Orphean Warbler go by unnoticed on the island.

Barred Warbler *(Sylvia nisoria)*. N.P. + Mall.: Busqueret esparverenc; C.: Tallarol esparverenc; Cast.: Curruca gavilana.

In September 1983 a young specimen was captured and ringed in S'Albufera. This was the first and only time this bird has been observed in Minorca.

The Barred Warbler has an Eastern Europe distribution.

Lesser Whitethroat *(Sylvia curruca)*. N.P.: Busqueret xerraire; Mall.: Busqueret xerraire; C.: Tallarol xerraire; Cast.: Curruca zarcerilla.

Only 2 observations have been recorded in Minorca, one in May '79 and another in April '84.

Their distribution area is central and eastern Europe, with only migration presence in other European countries.

Nevertheless we believe that there must be a few passage migrants each year that go by unnoticed.

Whitethroat (*Sylvia communis*). N.P.: Busqueret d'abatzer; A.M.: Busqueret gris; Mall.: Busqueret d'abatzer; C.: Tallareta vulgar; Cast.: Curruca zarcera.

A common migrator to Minorca, it is more abundant during spring passage (March to June), and scarce during the autumn passage.

During those months they can be found almost anywhere, being more abundant in coastal areas due to their short stopover.

This species has a Euro-Turkish distribution, and spends winters in Tropical Africa.

Garden Warbler (*Sylvia borin*). N.P.: Busqueret mosquiter; Mall.: Busqueret mosquiter; C.: Tallarol gros; Cast.: Curruca mosquitera.

Common passage migrant in Minorca during both spring/autumn passages. They can be observed between March and June and between August and October, registering the highest density in April/May and September. It is rather difficult to identify due to its quiet habits and discreet plumage.

Over 300 specimens have been ringed on the island, and only one was recovered in Finland.

As migratory birds they can be found around areas with a minimum amount of vegetation, coastal areas being most favourable. They breed around most of Europe and Western Asia, and migrate to South and Tropical Africa for winter.

Blackcap (*Sylvia atricapilla*). N.P.: Busqueret de capell; A.M.: Nyecra, capnegre; Mall.: Busqueret de capell; C.: Tallarol de casquet; Cast.: Curruca capirotada (**95**).

Blackcaps are present on the island all year round. The breeding population, probably sedentary, is not very abundant and is mainly located in wooded areas (pines-oaks).

During October and November there is a very intense migration passage, with numerous arrivals of winter visitors coming from Eu-

95. Blackcap *(Sylvia atricapilla)*

rope. From March to May there is another migration passage, although not as intense as the autumn one.

They feed on insects and other invertebrates and in autumn and winter also eat berries and fruit (wild or cultivated). They build their nest on tree-tops and bushes at an approximate height of 1.5 to 3 meters. They lay 4/6 eggs which are incubated during 12/13 days by both parents. They breed once or twice a year.

They are distributed all over Europe, Northeast Africa and Western Asia. During winter they migrate in massive numbers towards Mediterranean countries.

24 recoveries have taken place on the islands: 3 from France, 5 from Germany, 4 from Belgium, 6 from Switzerland, 3 from England, 1 from Holland, and 1 from Catalonia. On the other hand of the 2,000 Blackcaps ringed in Minorca, 3 have been recovered in Algeria and 2 in France.

Yellow-browed Warbler *(Phylloscopus inornatus)*. N.P.: Ull de bou billistat; C.: Mosquiter de doble ratlla; Cast.: Mosquitero bilistado.

Only one registration was noted during the migration ringing campaigns in Es Prat de S'Albufera, on October 18th, 1989. This species breeds in Siberia and Eastern Asia, most years there are records in Western Europe, mainly during autumn.

Wood Warbler *(Phylloscopus sibilatrix)*. N.P.: Ull de bou xiulaire; Mall.: Ull de bou xiulaire; C.: Mosquiter xiulaire; Cast.: Mosquitero silbador.

A common spring migrant during April and May, during autumn few are recorded and are therefore considered rare at this time. Their stay on the island is brief, just to rest and eat, this is why strong fluctuations occur from one day to the next.

As a migrant, it can be found anywhere with a minimum amount of vegetation, but they mainly concentrate in coastal and wet areas, where they find mosquitoes and other insects, their classical diet. In Europe they are summer residents, breeding mainly in Central Europe, migrating to Tropical Africa (above the Equator).

Chiffchaff (*Phylloscopus collybita*). N.P.: Ull de bou (comú); A.M.: Ullet de bou; Mall.: Ullet de bou; C.: Mosquiter comú; Cast.: Mosquitero común **(96)**.

Present as passage migrant and winter resident. The autumn passage is much larger than the spring passage, being especially intense from mid-October to mid-November although the first visitors start arriving in August.

96. Chiffchaff *(Phylloscopus collybita)*

During spring, April is the month when it is most noticeable. The Chiffchaff is commonly found near wet areas, where they find large amounts of mosquitoes. They fly about orchards and gardens, and really anywhere with a minimum vegetation. It is very active, and continuously moves around bushes, trees, tall grass, capturing insects as it flies. A tame bird, it can be observed from a close distance.

They breed all round Europe and Northwest Africa, migrating to Mediterranean countries for winter.

27 ringed specimens have been recovered, 10 from Germany, 10 from Switzerland, 4 from France, 2 from Holland, 1 from for-mer Yugoslavia.

Out of the over 1,000 ringed in Minorca only 2 have been recovered in Algeria.

Willow Warbler (*Phylloscopus trochilus*). N.P.: Ull de bou de passa; Mall.: Ull de bou gros; C.: Mosquiter de passa; Cast.: Mosquitero musical.

Very similar in aspect to the Chiffchaff, this species is a passage migrant on the island, especially during the spring passage, since it is more scarce in autumn.

They start to arrive in March, but the busiest times of arrival are between mid-April to mid-May. Some specimens may remain in Minorca till June.

In Minorca the Willow Warbler is found in the same habitats as the Chiffchaff.

They mainly breed in Central and Northern Europe and migrate to Africa in winter. 7 ringed specimens have been recovered in the Balearics, 2 from England, 1 from Holland, 1 from Switzerland, 1 from Belgium, and 1 from Germany.

Bonelli's Warbler (*Phylloscopus bonelli*). N.P.: Ull de bou pàl·lid; Mall.: Ull de bou pàl·lid; C.: Mosquiter pàl·lid; Cast.: Mosquitero papialbo.

It has only been recorded 6 times in Minorca. It is very possible that a few specimens stopover on migrations and go by unnoticed.

Since their distribution area is Mediterranean and they breed in countries surrounding the Balearics, this leads us to believe that they try to avoid the sea.

Goldcrest (*Regulus regulus*). N.P.: Reietó; A.M.: ropitet; Mall.: Reietó; C.: Reietó; Cast.: Reyezuelo sencillo.

The Goldcrest visits Minorca during migration and in winter, generally in moderate numbers.

The truth is that the Goldcrest is a very unknown bird on the island, no studies have been made on it.

They spend a lot of time in woods, in tall trees, which makes them difficult to observe. Only occasionally, when moving around bushes, can one observe them close-up, and they become very tame.

They are mainly found near pines and oak woods, and on occasions even in orchards and gardens.

The Goldcrest breeds all over Europe and migrates to the south in winter.

In Minorca a Goldcrest ringed in Finland was found which is admirable, taking into account that this bird hardly weighs more than 5 grams.

Firecrest (*Regulus ignicapillus*). N.P.: Reietó cellablanca; A.M.: Ropitet cellablanca, r. pintat; Mall: Reietó cellablanca; C.: Bruel; Cast.: Reyezuelo listado. **(97)**.

The Firecrest is present in Minorca all year around, they breed in pine and oak woods, and are quite difficult to observe. Possibly most of the Minorcan population is sedentary, in winter they move to other habitats on the island.

97. Firecrest *(Regulus ignicapillus)*

It hasn't yet been confirmed, but it is quite possible that some European specimens migrate to the island in winter.

Previous authors considered the species endemic *(Regulus ignicapillus balearicus)*. This fact hasn't recently been revised. This species has similar habits to the Goldcrest, both species feed on insects and spiders which they capture amongst tree leaves and bushes.

The nest (rather difficult to see) is a small bag hanging from a branch. This bag is built with spider webs and fine grass. They lay 7/11 eggs (obviously very tiny) which are incubated during 14/15 days by the female. Usually they breed twice a year.

Firecrests, like many other small birds, are very sensitive to cold winters, which may lead to high mortality rates.

FAMILY MUSICAPIDAE

Spotted Flycatcher *(Muscicapa striata)*. N.P.: Menjamosques; A.M.: Capsoti, caçamosques, matamosques, papamosques; Mall.: Caçamosques; C.: Papamosques gris; Cast.: Papamoscas gris **(98)**.

The Spotted Flycatcher is a non abundant summer breeder and passage migrant in Minorca.

They arrive in April, and the migration passage lasts till May. During this time the breeders are intermingled with migrating ones. But the autumn passage is not as noticeable as the spring passage.

From left to right and top to bottom:
19.- Turtle Dove *(Streptopelia turtur)* (Photo R.V.)
20.- Razorbill *(Alca torda)* Port of Maó Nov.1985 (Photo R.V.)
21.- Barn Owl *(Tyto alba)* 3 Full grown juveniles at nest. (Photo R.V.)
22.- Scops Owl *(Otus scops)*. (Photo R.V.)
23.- Hoopoe *(Upupa epops)* (Photo R.V.)

98. Spotted flycatcher
(Muscicapa striata)

These passerine are easy to observe and have peculiar habits. They perch on a spot with good visibility where they wait for flies. After each capture, they return to the same perch, or one nearby. Their ideal habitat is nearby woods, but they tend to visit orchards and gardens too.

They build their nests in bushes or trees (sometimes on rural buildings), never too high up, and lay 4/5 eggs which the mother incubates between 11 to 15 days.

Red-breasted Flycatcher *(Ficedula parva)*. N.P.: Menjamosques menut; Mall.: Menjamosques barba-roja; C.: Papamosques menut; Cast.: Papamoscas papirrojo.

In Minorca we have one observation recorded in April 1984. Almost every year there is one observation or capture on the eastern coast of Spain or the islands, although it is a species of eastern distribution.

Collared Flycatcher *(Ficedula albicollis)*. N.P.: Menjamosques de collar; Mall.: Menjamosques de collar; C.: Papamosques de collar; Cast.: Papamoscas collarino.

Very few observations recorded, and so far they have always taken place in April. Their distribution area is around eastern Europe, this and the lack of recent observations or captures during scientific ringing campaigns makes us think that this species is an accidental migrant to the island.

From left to right and top to bottom:
24.- Fan-Tailed Warbler *(Cisticola juncidis)* (Photo F.P.)
25.- Sardinian Warbler at nest with chicks *(Sylvia melanocephala)* (Photo F.P.)
26.- Stonechat *(Saxicola torquata)* (Photo F.P.)
27.- Woodchat Shrike *(Lanius senator)* (Photo F.P.)

Pied Flycatcher (*Ficedula hypoleuca*). N.P.: Menjamosques negre; A.M.: Xipret **negre**, papamosques, menjafigues; Mall.: Menjamosques negre; C.: **Mas-**tegatatxes; Cast.: Papamoscas cerrojillo **(99)**.

A common **passage** migrant abundant during April, May and September, and less numerous during March/June/August and October.

The Pied **Flycatcher** has similar habits to the spotted flycatcher. During migration periods it can be observed anywhere with vegetation, their favorite spots being orchards and coastal areas.

It has occasionally bred in Majorca, and it could sporadically occur here, but it has never been detected.

99. Pied Flycatcher (*Ficedula hypoleuca*)

Their distribution and breeding areas are north-western Africa, most of Europe and western Asia. They migrate to Tropical Africa for winter.

On the Balearics two ringed Pied Flycatchers, have been retrieved, one from Russia and one from Finland.

FAMILY PARIDAE

Great Tit (*Parus major*). N.P.: Primavera; A.M.: Ferrer, ferreret; Mall.: Cap ferrerico; C.: Mallarenga carbonera; Cast.: Carbonero común. **(100)** (Photo 28).

Great Tits are year-round residents in Minorca and although they are not abundant they are quite well spread out over the island. Their ideal habitat are forests, but they can be observed around orchards, gardens and steep river banks.

They can easily be observed and tend to imitate songs and calls of other species. Their main source of nourishment are invertebrates and some vegetable matter, fruit and seeds (during fall). Around the Balearics they tend to consume caterpillars (a good method for controlling this plague).

Around Europe they tend to visit gardens where they feed from the artificial feeding-boxes that most families install in their gardens.

To make a nest they take advantage of holes in trees, rocks, and dry stone walls, buildings etc... And they make good use of nest-boxes (produced by man for this purpose).

They can lay up to 12 eggs, the incubation period lasts for about 13/14 days. They breed once or twice each season.

100. Great Tit *(Parus major)*

FAMILY TICHODROMADIDAE

Wallcreeper *(Tichodroma muraria)*. N.P.: Pela-roques; A.M.: Roquer; Mall + C.: Pela-roques; Cast.: Treparriscos. **(101)**.

Only seven observations have been recorded in Minorca: one in August, 2 in December, one in January and 3 in March. We have subsequently classified them as occasional autumn to spring visitors.

Their distribution area is North Africa, Southeastrn Europe and Central Asia. They live in mountain rocky areas, which makes sense, as all Minorcan observations have taken place on river banks,

101. Wallcreeper *(Tichodroma muraria)* walls and cliffs.

FAMILY REMIZIDAE

Penduline Tit *(Remiz pendulinus)*. N.P.: Teixidor; A.M.: Coeta llarga; Mall + C.: Coeta llarga; Cast.: Pájaro moscón **(102)**.

The first record in Minorca of the Penduline Tit dates from 1977, since then it has been recorded most winters but in small numbers.

No doubt that this factor is related to the expansion phase that Penduline Tits are going through at present. This has been noted in Majorca also.

102. Penduline Tit *(Remiz pendulinus)*

Observations and captures have taken place between October and April. The best areas in Minorca are Prat de Son Bou, Prat de S'Albufera and Prat de Son Saura Nord.

They have discreet habits but a very characteristic call. They are normally found in small groups, moving about reed-beds etc.. searching for insects and fruit.

FAMILY ORIOLIDAE

Golden Oriole *(Oriolus oriolus)*. N.P.: Oriol; A.M.: Menjafigues, tord groc; Mall. + C.: Oriol; Cast.: Oropéndola.

A scarce passage migrant more frequent during spring migration (April-May). As a migrant it can be observed anywhere but tends to prefer open spaces with scattered trees spread around. Figtrees are a favorite especially in September when fruit is ripe.

Solitary specimens are mostly observed. During the summer breeding periods it is present all over Europe and migrates to Tropical Africa in winter.

FAMILY LANIIDAE

Red-backed Shrike *(Lanius collurio)*. N.P.: Capsigrany roig; A.M.: Capsigrany ala-rotja; Mall.: Capsigrany d'esquena roja; C.: Escorxador; Cast.: Alcaudón dorsirrojo.

Only 3 observations recorded in Minorca, which isn't unusual since this species doesn't like flying over open sea.

They breed all over continental Europe and migrate following eastern routes.

Great Grey Shrike *(Lanius excubitor)*. N.P.: Capsigrany reial; A.M.: Capsigrany gris; Mall.: Capxerigany reial; C.: Botxí; Cast.: Alcaudón real.

This species has a status of rare vagrant visitor to Minorca. Only two observations have been recorded (July 77/Jan 90). This bird is present all over Europe and North Africa, but all populations are sedentary, only northern European specimens move slightly south in winter.

Woodchat Shrike (*Lanius senator*). N.P.: Capsigrany (comú); A.M.: Capsoti, Quequec, Capxerigany; Mall.: Capxerigany; C.: Capsigrany; Cast.: Alcaudón común (**103**) (Photo 27).

They arrive in Minorca towards March and remain till October. During March-April and September a migratory passage of the *senator* subspecies is identified. The breeders all belong to subspecies *badius*. The woodchat shrike is very common around all Minorcan habitats, absent only in areas of scarce vegetation.

Ecologically, they act as effective predators, killing a large selection of small animals: little birds

103. Woodchat Shrike *(Lanius senator)*

(which they usually deca-pitate), mice, little snakes, geckoes, lizards, frogs, insects (large grasshoppers) and many other inver-tebrates. Sometimes they rivet their victims against prickly bushes in order to use this as a food stock.

They are really aggressive and do not hesitate to attack other large birds that might fly too close to their nests.

They perch on trees, bushes, walls, poles, power cables etc.. from where they control their surroundings, throwing themselves upon any pray coming within a close distance.

The nests are built in trees and bushes, often at a reasonable height. They lay 4/7 eggs which are incubated by the mother during 15/16 days. They may lay twice a year. Their distribution area is Mediterranean and migrate to Tropical Africa for the winter.

A bird ringed in Majorca was recovered in Tunisia.

FAMILY CORVIDAE

Chough (*Pyrrhocorax pyrrhocorax*). N.P.: Gralla de bec vermell; Mall + C.: Gralla de bec vermell; Cast.: Chova piquirroja.

Only 2 observations recorded in Minorca: 1 in October 1946, and one in February 1987. It is an exceptional visitor to the island.

Rook (*Corvus frugilegus*). N.P.: Graula; Mall.: Gralla pelada; C.: Graula; Cast.: Graja.

An exceptional visitor, only two captures have taken place in Minorca, one is embalmed in the Ateneum Museum and the other is in a private collection.

Raven (*Corvus corax*). N.P.+ Mall + C.: Corb; Cast.: Cuervo. **(104)** (Photo 33).

104. Raven *(Corvus corax)*

During the last 15 years there has been a drastic drop of the Raven population in Minorca (between 60/80%). This has coincided with the decrease of red kites, both species have similar habits and feed on carrion.

There must be many reasons for this, but there isn't enough information to evaluate it accurately.

The raven is possibly the most intelligent bird in the world.

It often comes into conflict with farmers' economical interests. For example, a lot of farmers say that when lambs are being born ravens are hovering over awaiting to kill the newborn.

They proceed by eating their soft parts such as eyes, tongue, and genitals, in front of their helpless mothers.

We don't know of any ornithologist who has ever seen this taking place, but we feel that it is common amongst ravens to wait for the placenta to break in order to eat it or to devour the still-born (occasionally lambs are born dead). Other farmers have told stories about how Ravens, during the summer, have literally attacked melon and watermelon plantations, picking away at each one in a nasty and devastating way.

In any case, these and other exaggerated stories created by the country folk have contributed to the massive killing of these birds by various indiscriminate methods which have also affected other species.

Another reason for the great decrease of the species is due to the lack of wild rabbits which was part of their natural diet.

Another interesting feature of Ravens is that they have a certain fun-loving attitude towards life. In fact they are even capable of learning to talk and modulate their voices.

A very interesting observation made by a Scottish ornithologist and published in a prestigious English magazine on ornithology describes the case of a Raven who repeatedly "tobogganed down an icy slope" in the heart of the countryside.

Going back to the Raven's food habits, they are fairly omnivorous and opportunistic, but basically they eat carrion, therefore it is frequent to see them around garbage dumps, competing with gulls and red kites.

As of December Ravens commence their acrobatic nuptial flights. They breed on cliff sides both inland and on the coast, and occasionally in trees. Their nests are built with dry twigs. They lay 4/6 eggs which are incubated by the female during 20/21 days. Abandoned nests are usually taken over by other species such as kestrels.

In Minorca these birds seem to be sedentary, and possibly a few youngsters leave the island during their first two years of life.

Between September and February they can be observed in large flocks searching for food during the day and going towards the dormitories at dusk.

FAMILY STURNIDAE

Starling (*Sturnus vulgaris*). N.P.+ Mall. + C.: Estornell; Cast.: Estornino pinto (**105**).

This bird is one of the mostly abundant in winter. It normally arrives at the beginning of September increasing until well into November.

105. Starling *(Sturnus vulgaris)*

It is a winter resident and a passage migrant. Most specimens are observed during the months of September/October and March to May are migrants.

Solitary specimens and small groups have been seen occasionally during summer but have never bred here. However, it seems that a pair or two have bred in Majorca.

This gregarious species tends to form large clouds sticking together in order to protect themselves from birds of prey.

During the day starlings disperse in groups around the countryside and amongst cattle, as they feed off invertebrates and fruit, such as wild olives. In fact this species becomes a plague for olive trees during harvesting.

Their traditional dormitories are located in Prat de Son Bou, Prat de S'Albufera and in forests in the center of the island.

It is distributed almost all over Europe, migrating to the Mediterranean countries in winter. Here in the Balearics more than 80 ringed starlings have been recovered: 41 from Switzerland, 12 from Germany, 7 from Czechoslovakia, 8 from France, 3 from Belgium, 4 from Poland, 1 from Italy, 1 from Russia, and one from the former Yugoslavia; this clearly reflects the origins of the winter residents.

Spotless Starling (*Sturnus unicolor*). N.P.: Estornell negre; Mall. + C.: Estornell negre; Cast.: Estornino negro.

Only half a dozen observations have been registered in Minorca in the past, referring to small groups between February and March.

This specimen is distributed all over Spain, northwest Africa, Corsica, Sardinia, and Sicily. It is basically sedentary, with short winter movements. However, they seem to intermingle with other starlings consequently passing unnoticed.

Rose-coloured Starling (*Sturnus roseus*). N.P.: Estornell rosat; Mall.: + C.: Estornell rosat; Cast.: Estornino rosado.

Exceptional on the island, the only existing reference is of a young specimen preserved at the Ateneum Museum.

It is a bird of eastern distribution which has only been observed on few occasions in Western Europe.

FAMILY PASSERIDAE

House Sparrow (*Passer domesticus*). N.P.: Pardal; A.M.: Pardal culoti (els joves); Mall.: Teulader; C.: Pardal comú; Cast.: Gorrión común **(106)** (Photo 32).

Well-known to every-body, they are abundant in villages, towns and rural areas; they feed on animal or vegetal leftovers. In the country they visit stables, chicken pens etc. where food is plentiful. "Wilder" ones eat fruit, seeds, insects and other invertebrates (mainly during spring and summer).

106. House Sparrow *(Passer domesticus)*

They live on cliffs, both inland and coastal (especially steep river banks), taking advantage of natural holes for breeding., and in towns and villages they use any large enough hole to make a nest. They use trees, poles and abandoned nests built by other birds. They lay twice or three times a season, between 3/6 eggs that both parents incubate 11 to 14 days.

This species is sedentary; during autumn and winter they move a little but never too far away from their breeding habitats. They tend to get together in large groups to sleep in the evening, usually in trees.

They are frequent prey to barn owls.

This species has extended its distribution area worldwide following the presence of man.

Tree Sparrow (*Passer montanus*). N.P.: Pardal barraquer; A.M.: Pardal moro, P. de bardissa; C.: pàrdal xarrec; Cast.: Gorrión molinero **(107)**.

The Tree Sparrow has only been observed on few occasions, during passage migrations and in winter, always solitary specimens or small groups.

Their distribution is all around most Europe and Asia, and it is basically sedentary, that is why they are only occasional visitors to Minorca.

107. Tree Sparrow *(Passer montanus)*

Rock Sparrow *(Petronia petronia)*.
N.P.: Pardal roquer; A.M.: P. boig, p. cridaire; Mall.: Gorrió foraster; C.: Pardal roquer; Cast.: Gorrión chillón.

Only 5 observations have been recorded on the island, one of which refers to a group singing in the steep river banks of Algendar in July 1974, which makes us think that year it could have bred in these areas. But no recent captures or observations have taken place.

This is a sedentary species with a distribution area in southern Europe, north Africa and eastern countries.

This bird is common around the other Balearic islands, Ibiza and Formentera. In Majorca a few small colonies are known which makes us think that it might pass Minorca unnoticed.

Snow Finch *(Montifringilla nivalis)*. N.P.: Pardal alablanc; Mall.: gorrió d'ala blanca; C.: Pardal alablanc; Cast.: Gorrión alpino.

Only registered once in Minorca, in the winter 1992/3, when a single specimen remained for a few days in Cap de Cavalleria.

This bird's habitats are mainly around mountains in the South of Europe and Asia, where it is sedentary. Exceptionally small groups can be observed in Majorcan mountains.

FAMILY FRINGILLIDAE

Chaffinch *(Fringilla coelebs)*. N.P. + Mall. + C.: Pinsà; Cast.: Pinzón vulgar **(108)**.

A common resident and abundant winter visitor, the local population is sedentary and is located around wooded areas all over the island, in pine and oak woods. They visit orchards and steep river banks too. During winters they tend to visit open fields.

108. Chaffinch *(Fringilla coelebs)*

They feed on seeds, grain, fruit, insects, worms.

They build their nests in high tree tops, making them difficult to see.

They lay 4/5 eggs, which are incubated by females during 11/13 days. They breed between March and July, once or sometimes twice.

In the Balearics 22 ringed specimens have been retrieved: 13 from Switzerland, 3 from Finland, 3 from Russia and one from France.

Brambling *(Fringilla montifringilla)*. N.P.: Pinsà mè; A.M.: Pinsà mec, P. reial, p. boig; Mall.: Pinsà mè; C.: Pinsà mec; Cast.: Pinzón real **(109)**.

A scarce but regular winter resident, observations take place from October to February and early March.

They often patrol in flocks intermingled with chaffinches around fields close to wooded areas, moving and perching in

109. Brambling *(Fringilla montifringilla)*

and around the trees. The best areas to observe them from are the surroundings of Lluriac, Prat de S'Albufera, La Vall etc..

They breed in Siberia and Northern Europe and migrate south in winter. Logically, the colder the winter is, the more abundant they are around our latitudes. A Brambling ringed in Switzerland and another one from Italy have been retrieved in the Balearics.

Serin *(Serinus serinus)*. N.P.: Serí; A.M.: Gafarró, lugret; Mall. + C.: Gafarró; Cast.: Verdecillo **(110)**.

Migrant and winter residents in Minorca. Their favorite spots are outskirts of forests, orchards and gardens, they move around in flocks intermingled with other finches.

Their distribution is Mediterranean (Northwest Africa and Central Europe and Asia). The northern specimens migrate to the Mediterranean for winter.

In Majorca and Ibiza they are present all year around, and also breed, which is curious as they are only passage migrants and winter residents on the island.

A ringed specimen in Switzerland and another one in Italy were retrieved in Majorca.

110. Serin *(Serinus serinus)*

Citril Finch *(Serinus citrinella)*. N.P.: Llucareta; Mall.: Verderol menut; C.: Llucareta; Cast.: Verderón serrano.

An exceptional visitor, only one observation is recorded on the island, in January 1983. Four specimens were seen in Son Bou.

They distribute around mountain areas of Southwestern Europe where they are sedentary.

Greenfinch *(Carduelis choris)*. N.P.: Verderol; Mall.: Verderol; C.: Verdum; Cast.: Verderón común **(111)** (Photo 31).

Very common in Minorca, they can be found anywhere with a minimun amount of trees: woods, orchards, gardens, steep river banks. During winter they venture into open country spaces often in mixed flocks with other finches.

They eat seeds, grains, fruit and insects during breeding season.

111. Greenfinch *(Carduelis chloris)*

They build nests in tall trees, where they lay 4/6 eggs which are incubated by the female during 12 to 14 days. They breed twice and occasionally 3 times a season (March to July).

Most Minorcan Green-finches are sedentary, but there is a small migration passage and a few winter residents from other areas.

There are records of a ringed Greenfinch from Switzerland retrieved here. And 3 greenfinches ringed in Majorca were found, two in France and one in Algeria.

Goldfinch (*Carduelis carduelis*). N.P.: Cadernera; A.M.: Caternera; Mall:: Cadernera; C.: Cadernera; Cast.: Jilguero **(112)**.

The goldfinch is a very sought-after bird by farmers or town people in order to cage them to enjoy their beautiful songs. They were even captured in large scales in order to be exported for commercial purposes to mainland Spain. They are also used by canary breeders to obtain hybrids. Although this species is now protected by law, these habits still remain.

112. Goldfinch *(Carduelis carduelis)*

Personally we would rather enjoy them in their natural habitat, where they are free to proceed with their ecological functions.

The Goldfinch is an abundant bird on the island and can be observed around pinewoods, orchards, gardens and open fields. They frequent road sides.

Outside the breeding season they fly intermingled with other finches searching for seeds and fruit, the base of their diet, which depending on the season is enhanced by insects. They especially enjoy nettle-seeds, so abundant around the Minorcan countryside.

Breeding season takes place between March and July, when they breed twice or even 3 times. Nests are built in trees, and they lay 4/6 eggs which the female incubates during 13 days.

The Goldfinch is basically sedentary on the island, and according to Moll they belong to the *parva* subspecies.

During migration periods a few outsiders can be present and according to Moll they belong to the *carduelis* subspecies.

Out of over 1,000 ringed Goldfinches in Minorca, not one has been retrieved abroad.

Siskin (*Carduelis spinus*). N.P.: Lugro; Mall.: Lleonet; C.: Lluer; Cast.: Lúgano **(113)**.

113. Siskin *(Carduelis spinus)*

The Siskin is a passage migrant on the island and also winter resident; its abundance varies according to the years. In general they can be observed from October to April.

They normally travel in intermingled flocks (with other finches), visiting farmlands, orchards, woods etc.

11 ringed recoveries prove their origins: 5 from Germany, 2 from Russia, 2 from England, 1 from former Czechoslovakia and one from Sweden.

Linnet (*Carduelis cannabina*). N.P.: Passerell; A.M.: Passerell reial, p. mallorquí (ssp. *cannabina*), passerell (ssp. *nana*); Mall + C.: Passerell; Cast.: Pardillo común **(114)**.

Common local breeders, they frequent open spaces, and rocky fields with low vegetation.

The local population is mostly sedentary, and according to Moll belong to the *nana* subspecies. (This author mentions that old hunters claimed there were 3 local subspecies, which is rather doubtful).

During winter there is an important number of visitors (belonging to the nominal subspecies, according to Moll), making them more abundant during this time of year.

114. Linnet
(Carduelis cannabina)

They breed between March and July, two and sometimes even three times. The nests are built on medium size bushes. They lay 4/6 eggs which the mother incubates during 10/14 days.

They are always in groups searching for food (seeds, fruit or insects). The winter visitors come mainly from Central Europe, as is reflected by the 36 ringed recoveries: 25 from Germany, 9 from Switzerland, 1 from Luxembourg and one from Belgium.

Redpoll (*Carduelis flammea*). N.P. + Mall. + C.: Passerell golanegra; Cast.: Pardillo sizerín.

There is only reference to one specimen ringed near Alaior in December 1988, and it is suspected that it was a runaway (there were rumors that some canary breeders had imported some specimens that year).

However, the natural presence of this bird is possible, although always of accidental or vagrant specimens. Their closest breeding area is the Alps, but it is known that they migrate south during severe winters. There is a recorded bibliographic reference of their presence in the Balearics during the winter 1959/60.

Common Crossbill (*Loxia curvirrostra*). N.P.: Trencapinyons; A.M.: Escardapinyes bectort; Mall.: Trencapinyons; C.: Trecapinyes; Cast.: Piquituerto común.

An exceptional visitor, there have been no recorded observations within the last 20 years. Past ornithologists had classified this bird as a scarce local resident (Munn 1924/31).

This bird is abundant in Majorca, but in Minorca it can only be classed as exceptional visitor.

Bullfinch (*Pyrrhula pyrrhula*). N.P. + Mall. + C.: Pinsà borroner; Cast.: Camachuelo común.

Five specimens were observed around Es Barranc d'Algendar in January 1977. This is the only known observation on the island. They breed in areas of Northern Spain and Europe. Some populations are migratory (or rather irruptive).

Trumpeter Finch (*Bucanetes githagineus*). N.P. + Mall. + C.: Pinsà trompeter; Cast.: Camachuelo trompetero.

One specimen was captured and ringed on the Illa de l'Aire during a ringing campaign in spring of 1993. This was the first and only time that this bird was detected around the Balearics. They breed in arid areas of Eastern Spain and Northern Africa, where they are local residents.

Hawfinch (*Coccothraustes coccothraustes*). N.P.: Bec-gros; A.M.: Bec de ferro, tord-bec; Mall. + C.: Durbec; Cast.: Picogordo (**115**).

Scarce winter residents and passage migrants, they are normally observed alone or in small groups of up to four specimens, from the

115. Hawfinch
(*Coccothraustes coccothraustes*)

end of October till March. They have been observed practically around all the island's different habitats, favouring wooded areas. With their strong beak they can break open certain fruits in order to eat the seeds.

Their distribution is in most of Europe, central and eastern Asia and North Africa.

FAMILY EMBERIZIDAE

Snow Bunting (*Plectrophenax nivalis*). N.P.: Sit blanc; Mall.: Hortolà blanc; C.: Sit blanc; Cast.: Escribano nival.

Exceptional visitor, there is only one reference of a captured specimen during December 76, around Mercadal. It is kept embalmed in a private collection.

This bird has an arctic distribution, in Europe it breeds in Iceland, Northern Scandinavia, Scotland and eastern Russia. In winter they migrate south of their distribution area but hardly ever reach Mediterranean latitudes.

Only about 10 observations have been recorded in the Balearics.

Yellowhammer (Yellow Bunting) (*Emberiza citrinella*). N.P.: Sit groc; Mall.: Hortolà groc; C.:Verderola; Cast.: Escribano cerillo.

An occasional visitor during migration periods and in winter. There are two confirmed observations in Minorca: One captured

From left to right and up to down:
28.- Great Tit (*Parus major*) (Photo F.P.)
29.- Robin (*Erithacus rubecula*)(Photo R.V.)
30.- Pied/white Wagtail (*Motacilla alba*)(Photo T.V.)
31.- Greenfinch (*Carduelis chloris*)(Photo R.V.)

specimen in January 1914 and another one in winter 74. In the rest of the Balearics it has been quoted more often but is considered an occasional visitor.

This bird has a Palearctic distribution and breeds in most of Europe and Asia. They are short distance migratory birds that move towards the south during winter.

Cirl Bunting (*Emberiza cirlus*). N.P.: Sit coll-negre; Mall.: Hortolà coll-negre; C.: Gratapalles; Cast.: Escribano soteño.

Accidental to Minorca, there is reference of a hunted specimen in June 1918 which is embalmed in the Ateneo Museum.

This species has a Mediterranean distribution, but is sedentary and doesn't fly great distances.

They are common residents in Majorca, and the lack of presence in Minorca is possibly due to biogeographical reasons as is the case in other species.

Rock Bunting (*Emberiza cia*). N.P.: Sit negre; Mall: Hortolà negre; C.: Sit negre; Cast.: Escribano montesino.

There are only two references on the island, and they are both doubtful. However they are scarce but regular winter visitors in Majorca.

Ortolan Bunting (*Emberiza hortulana*). N.P.: Hortolà; A.M.: Súl.lera dels vergers; Mall. + C.: Hortolà; Cast.: Escribano hortelano.

During the last 20 years this bird has been quoted about a dozen times in different areas, during the months of April, May, August and September.

This bird breeds all round Europe and migrates to Africa in winter. No doubt it passes through the island in small numbers during migration periods.

From left to right and up to down:
32.- House Sparrow (*Passer domesticus*), male (Photo R.V.)
33.- Raven (*Corvus corax*) (Photo R.V.)
34.- Cormorants (*Phalacrocorax carbo*), and an immature Flamingo (*Phoenicopterus ruber*) in S'Albufera (Photo F.P.)
35.- Ringing a Water Rail (*Rallus aquaticus*) at Prat de S'Albufera (Photo R.V.)

Red Bunting (*Emberiza schoeniclus*). N.P.: Sit de canyís; A.M.: Súl·lera de prat, butzac; Mall.: Hortolà de canyar; C.: Repica-talons; Cast.: Escribano palustre **(116)**.

The Red Bunting in Minorca is a passage migrant and winter resident, in moderate and fluctuating numbers.

The winter residents stay from November to March, and recorded observations before or after these dates correspond to migrant specimens.

116. Red Bunting *(Emberiza schoeniclus)*

Their favorite habitats are reed-beds (Son Bou and S'Albufera), orchards near steep river banks, with reed-beds nearby to go to sleep.

Corn Bunting (*Miliaria calandra*). N.P.: Súl·lera; A.M.: Sól·lera; Mall: Sól·lera; C.: Cruixidell; Cast.: Triguero. **(117)**

An abundant local resident, present all year round. Their ideal habitat are fields with nearby trees. They perch on trees and high spots from where they sing. They build their nest on the ground amongst vegetation and bushes. They lay between 4 and 6 eggs which the female incubates during 13 days. Each female lays twice a year. The males are polygamous.

Outside breeding season they get together in the evenings to go to sleep.

They eat insects, worms, little snails, seeds, grains and wild fruit.

117. Corn Bunting *(Miliaria calandra)*

NOTE

While this book was being published we received information from various British Ornithologists of the RSPB, who accounted for various interesting observations made on the island. Among these we have to point out the ones that make reference to species under observation for the first time.

Pygmy Cormorant (*Phalacrocorax pygmaeus*). It was seen in S'Albufera from the 8th to the 13th September 1986. The closest breeding habitats are found in Greece.

Saker (*Falco cherrug*). One was observed in the morning of September 13th 1986 flying around Sta. Àgueda, and during the afternoon (supposedly the same specimen) in S'Albufera, where it was observed for over one hour by the group of Ornithologists.

Olivaceous Warbler (*Hippolais pallida*). One specimen was observed on 30/9/87 and another one on 1/10/87, in different locations.

The head of this expedition was ornithologist Keith Fairclough. Although these annotations deserve full respect and support they will have to be approved by the "Comité ibérico de rarezas" of the S.E.O.

BIBLIOGRAPHY

Las aves de Menorca by Josep Moll Casasnovas. Published by Estudi General Lul.lià. Palma de Mallorca 1956.

Avifauna de Menorca by Jordi Muntaner, Josep Congost and others. Museu de Zoologia, Ajuntament de Barcelona 1984.

Guía de Incafo de las aves de la Península Ibérica y Baleares by Ramon Sáez-Royuela. INCAFO Madrid, 1980.

Enciclopèdia d'Història Natural dels Països Catalans, tom 12: Ocells various authors. Published by Fundació Enciclopèdia Catalana, Barcelona, 1986.

Anuaris ornitològics de les Balears, 1985 to 1992. Published by G.O.B.

Ardeola. Revista Ibérica de Ornitología. Sociedad Española de Ornitología, Madrid.

Ringing files from G.O.B.

Migración en aves; tratado teórico y práctico by F. Bernis, S.E.O. Madrid, 1966.

INDEX OF BIRDS[1]

[1] All numbers refer to pages; in roman for description, and in italics for bird's drawing

INDEX

MANUALS D'INTRODUCCIÓ A LA NATURALESA

CONÈIXER MALLORCA

(Llibres en llengua no catalana)

Elspeth Beckett. *Illustrated Flora of Mallorca*

Anthony Bonner. *Plants of the Balearic Islands*

Heidi Gildemeister. *Mediterranean Gardening*

Herbert W. Heinrich.

Band 1. *Wanderführer durch Mallorcas Südwest-Region.*
Mit Panoramakarten von Peguera und Andratx/Sant Telm

Band 2. *Wanderführer durch Mallorcas Südwest-Region.*
Mit Panoramakarten von der Serra de Na Burguesa bis zum Esclop

Band 3. *12 klassische Wanderungen durch Mallorca*

Band 4. *Das Mallorca Ludwig Salvators heute erlebt.*
Ausflüge in die Vergangenheit auf den Spuren des Erzherzogs.

Band 5. *Mallorca Erlebnisbuch*

Band 6. *Verliebt in Mallorca.* Geschichten und Feuilletons reich illustriert

Band 7. *12 Abenteuer-Wanderungen durch Mallorcas Berge.*
Mit Panoramakarten und vielen Illustrationen

Band 8. *10 schöne wenig bekannte Wanderungen auf Mallorca.*
Mit anschaulichen Panoramakarten und vielen Illustrationen

Herbert W. Heinrich. *12 classic Hikes through Mallorca*

Herbert W. Heinrich. *Doce excursiones clásicas por Mallorca*

Herbert W. Heinrich. *La Mallorca del Archiduque Luis Salvador*

Herbert W. Heinrich. *Doce excursiones-aventura en las montañas de Mallorca*

Johanna Jachmann. *Mallorca für Kinder. Ich zeige Euch meine Insel*

Armand Llinarès. *Raymund Lulle*

Joan Mayol. *The Birds of the Balearic Islands*

Toby Molenaar. *Discovering the Art of Mallorcan Cookery*

Donald G. Murray. *Fincas rústicas de las Baleares*

Benigne Palos. *Itinerarios de montaña*

Juan Poyatos. *Guía de la bicicleta de montaña. Excursiones en Mallorca*

Juan Poyatos. *Guia de la bicicleta de muntanya.*

Alberto Quintana. *El sistema urbano de Mallorca*

Enric Ramos. *Birds of Menorca*

Carles Tudurí, Jaume Escandell i Jaume Marquès. *Mallorca en bici*

Pere Xamena Fiol. *Resumen de historia de Mallorca*

Fritz Söllheim. *Sklaven Piraten, Mallorca 1500-1800*

Juan Poyatos, Aníbal Alonso. *Bucear en Mallorca* (en preparació)